ONE WEEK LOAN
CONST

Ellis Baker

and

Dr Ronan Champion

Acknowledgments

Crown copyright material is reproduced with the permission of the Controller of HMSO and the Queen's Printer for Scotland.

Please note: References to the masculine include, where appropriate, the feminine.

Published by the Royal Institution of Chartered Surveyors (RICS)
Surveyor Court
Westwood Business Park
Coventry CV4 8JE
UK
www.ricsbooks.com

ISBN 978 1 84219 433 1

Typeset in Great Britain by Columns Design Ltd, Reading, Berks

Printed in Great Britain by Page Bros, Milecross Lane, Norwich

Printed on Greencoat Paper. Greencoat is produced using 80% recycled fibre and 20% virgin TCF pulp from sustainable forests.

Contents

Preface

Many cases come before the Technology and Construction Court where the dispute has arisen because of uncertainties created during the tendering process. The successful procurement of a project is difficult. Equally, it is not easy to have a proper overview of issues which need to be considered as part of the process. This book seeks to identify the difficulties in the process so that the risks can be identified and dealt with. That is not a simple task but, by concentrating on this comparatively narrow but important topic, Ellis Baker and Ronan Champion have achieved that goal and produced a comprehensive guide to the pitfalls in tendering and procurement.

The process of procurement not only has to consider the interests of the parties but also has to take account of increasing regulation and statutory intervention. The scope of the EU procurement regime is but one of the topics dealt with in this book. Whilst regulations in the field of public procurement set out detailed requirements for the tendering process, it is surprising how little consideration has been given, in this jurisdiction, to the mutual obligations of the parties during that process. Indeed, the concept of the tendering contract itself has, for many years, been relatively undeveloped. The authors deal fully with this important area, drawing on case law from a number of common law jurisdictions. The book is not limited to narrow issues of procurement. It also tackles and provides clear guidance on other more general questions, such as: what happens if you leave matters to be agreed, or if negotiations fail, or if there is only a letter of intent?

One of the best features of the books in the *Case in Point* series is the way in which they deal with the subject, and this book is no exception. This is not a dreary legal textbook but a practical reference book that allows users to obtain an immediate insight into an issue. It not only provides the necessary information in a concise way but, by including digests of relevant cases, it also allows the approach of the courts to be better understood.

In combining the knowledge and experience of Ellis Baker and Ronan Champion the result, as would be expected, is an accurate statement of the legal principles but with an emphasis on the practical application of those principles. For all Chartered Surveyors and other professionals concerned with the process of procurement in the construction, engineering and allied industries, this book provides an important addition to their shelves.

The Hon Sir Vivian Ramsey, 2008
The Technology and Construction Court

Introduction

A collection of over 140 reported cases on tendering and procurement issues might seem to provide strong evidence supporting the strictures of Sir Michael Latham in the mid-1990s regarding an industry riven by conflict and absence of trust. The lesson we derive from what is admittedly a daunting body of cases is that the procurement process is fraught with complexity and is becoming much more so.

Formation of contracts has always given rise to difficulties in English law, and not just in construction. In construction, the widespread and often indiscriminate use of letters of intent/letters of award/letters of appointment to facilitate early mobilisation of resources by a contractor or consultant has created many situations not capable of resolution by reference to the simple rules of offer and acceptance. Whether the contractor is working onsite under a contract at all is one question, but if the answer is yes, it begs further questions as to whether a standard form or other written agreement is incorporated, and if so which, or whether the terms of the contract are implied and, if so, what they are. If there is no express provision, the contractor will certainly want to know the basis, if any, of its entitlement to payment. The client may need to know its rights, if any, concerning defects in the construction in the event that the relationship terminates without the issue being addressed. So many uncertainties arise on the effect of letters of intent that another has been added to their number: the exposure to claims of professional negligence of a consultant who specifies their use.

The process of competitive tendering was traditionally entirely in the hands of the client letting the contract and its consultants. Cynics would say that there were, 50 years ago, hardly any rules constraining the client's freedom to decide how and what it liked. If that was true, it certainly is not now. The development of the tender contract, by which all contractors submitting conforming tenders acquire contractual protection of their rights and especially the advent of the EU procurement regime in the public sector and utilities industries have obliged clients to devise and observe sophisticated tendering procedures and to expect formidable challenges from disappointed tenderers if they do not.

The parties may even have adopted an agreement, which appears to provide for most eventualities, only to have it amended by statute or common law as not meeting legal requirements as to what a contract should or should not contain. Payment provisions, even those in widespread use, may offend against the *Housing Grants, Construction and Regeneration Act* 1996, at the time of writing undergoing long overdue revision in the *Construction Contracts Bill* 2008; agreed liquidated damages provisions might not survive the application of the rule against penalties.

So the cases serve to illustrate the difficulties of tendering and other aspects of procurement. But they have a much more positive purpose. They offer guidance on how to 'get it right' from the start. The factual scenarios of the cases themselves offer illustrations of bad practice and good. No one who has read the recent decision of the Northern Ireland High Court in *J&A Developments v Edina Manufacturing* would believe that it is acceptable to depart from a tendering procedure specified in the conditions of tender. No consultant reading *Picardi v Cuniberti* would try to introduce provision for adjudication in a contract with a private house-owner without explaining the provision to the client. Conversely, following the course of action adopted by the client's team in *Alfred McAlpine Capital Projects v Tilebox*, in calculating a liquidated damages figure based on the minimum weekly rental value of the completed building, would protect the provision against a contractor's allegation that it was a penalty clause. The preparatory work done, which some neglect, stood the client in good stead and would repay imitation.

Beyond the factual lessons, the more obvious purpose of the book is to provide clarification of the law through the decisions of the courts which make it. Thus *Steria v Sigma* offers a very recent application of the contra proferentem principle, emphasising the importance of ascertaining whether a term operates for the sole benefit of a particular party to the contract. *George Wimpey UK v VIC Construction* provides a re-statement of the requirements to be fulfilled if rectification of a written agreement is to be successfully claimed by a party on the basis of unilateral mistake. To their expositions of law judges can on occasion additionally offer robust common sense, which can be put into use by those reading their judgments and assimilating the advice offered. While His Honour Judge Coulson (as he then was) in *Cunningham v Collett & Farmer* naturally stopped short of saying that the choice of contract form for a project was immaterial, he did confirm that contract administrators are justified, and should be encouraged, in using particular standard forms with which they are familiar.

A review of cases may point to the past but also helps look to the future. As tendering and contractual arrangements have changed, so the cases have begun to follow: if in the past the courts faced single-stage tendering, they will increasingly face two-stage tendering, target cost contracts, Guaranteed Maximum Price arrangements, partnering, collaboration and good faith issues in the future.

This is the spirit in which the production of this book has been undertaken, and if it helps in making the lessons of past projects and clarifications of law by the courts more accessible to those in the construction professions who need them, it will have served its purpose.

Ellis Baker
Dr Ronan Champion
October 2008

List of Acts, Statutory Instruments and abbreviations

The following Acts and Statutory Instruments are referred to in this publication. Where an Act or Statutory Instrument is mentioned frequently, it is referred to by the abbreviation in brackets that follows.

Arbitration Act 1980

Competition Act 1998

Construction Contracts Bill 2008

Defective Premises Act 1972

Housing Grants, Construction and Regeneration Act 1996 **('HGCRA 1996')**

Judgments Act 1838

Late Payment of Commercial Debts (Interest) Act 1998

Partnership Act 1890

Sale and Supply of Goods Act 1994

Sale of Goods Act 1979

Supply of Goods and Services Act 1982

Unfair Contract Terms Act 1977

Public Contracts Regulations 2006

Public Services Contracts Regulations 1993

Public Works Contracts Regulations 1991

Unfair Terms in Consumer Contracts Regulations 1999

Utilities Contracts Regulations 1996

Utilities Contracts Regulations 2006

Housing Grants, Construction and Regeneration Act 1996 reform – the *Construction Contracts Bill* 2008

At the time of going to press, final consultation had just ended on the draft legislation to reform the *Housing Grants, Construction and Regeneration Act* 1996. Not all provisions are relevant to the substance of this book and the eventual content of the Act still is not certain, but in summary relevant points of change are as follows:

- the s. 107 requirement that provisions of the Act only apply to written contracts is to be abolished; oral and part-oral contracts will be included;

- parties will be prevented from contractually allocating costs before the appointment of adjudicator;

- ss. 110 and 111 payment and withholding notices are to be reformed; and

- attempts to bypass pay-when-paid provisions by such devices as pay-when-certified clauses will be rendered ineffective.

The text of this publication is divided into commentary and case summaries. The commentary is enclosed between grey highlighted lines for ease of reference.

Table of cases

Table of cases

1
Preparation/contract planning

The process of selecting a form of contract, inviting tenders, receiving and handing quotations with inconsistent terms, negotiations and finally letting a contract is not usually a period during which parties are in dispute. There may be much activity leading to contract award, all carried out in short periods of time under pressure to let a contract and start the works. It is later, when differing interpretations are attached to what work is required to be done or to payment or other terms, that parties reflect back on their pre-contract activities. It is at this point that the entire field of pre-contract activity can come under scrutiny. It can raise issues of concern to those who may have been directly involved in the same contract negotiations.

This section explores the judicial treatment of that pre-contract activity. It addresses the question whether regard can be had to pre-contract negotiations as part of the factual matrix when interpreting a contract's terms. It notes the difficulties that come from parties exchanging inconsistent quotations and acceptances, and asks which might dominate. If within the terms the parties have an agreement to agree some matter in the future, is it binding on the parties? This section concludes with a review of cases involving selection of contracts, and those cases where the court has been concerned to interpret whether the agreement was in writing.

1.1   NEGOTIATIONS AND THEIR LEGAL EFFECT

Where construction contracts are let following negotiations, issues can arise over the extent to which reference might be made to pre-contract negotiations as an aid to construction of the agreement or as an aid to interpretation of terms. Lord Wilberforce emphasised in *Rearden Smith Line Ltd v Hansen-Tangen* and *Prenn v Simmonds* the importance of the 'factual matrix'. That, in turn, raised issues as to whether a party could refer to matters that arose during negotiations as being within the factual matrix. It was noted in *VHE Construction Ltd v Alfred McAlpine Construction* that evidence of negotiations can be admitted for the purpose of identifying whether an agreement has been reached but not for determination of its terms (and see also *Bank of Scotland v Dunedin Property Investment Co Ltd*).

The leading proposition on interpretation, and particularly the extent to which contract negotiations might be referred to, was provided by Lord Hoffmann in *Investors Compensation Scheme v West Bromwich Building Society* and *BCCI v Ali* (Lord Bingham of Cornhill). There, the court determined that prior negotiations are not generally admissible. One exception, discussed in *ProForce Recruit Ltd v Rugby Group Ltd*, is the 'private dictionary inroad', where evidence of negotiations showed that the parties had agreed a particular meaning which had then been used in the contract without definition. In *Chartbrook Ltd v Persimmon Homes Ltd and others*, the court determined that prior negotiations are not admissible except in limited circumstances, i.e. cases of the 'private dictionary inroad'.

The decision in *Howgate Shopping Centre v Catercraft Services Ltd* refers to the position where parties have different states of knowledge of matters under negotiation. Ultimately, if one party positively misleads the other, it may result in an unenforceable agreement, as decided in *Commission for New Towns v Cooper*.

Reardon Smith Line Ltd v Hansen-Tangen (1976)

A point for consideration arose in the House of Lords as to the extent to which, when construing a construction contract, regard might be had to other documents in existence at the time, and to negotiations. Lord Wilberforce discussed the duty of a court which is called upon to construe a commercial contract:

> 'No contracts are made in a vacuum: there is always a setting in which they have to be placed. The nature of what

is legitimate to have regard to is usually described as the "surrounding circumstances" but this phrase is imprecise: it can be illustrated but hardly defined. In a commercial contract it is certainly right that the court should know the commercial purpose of the contract and this in turn presupposes knowledge of the genesis of the transaction, the background, the context, the market in which the parties are operating. ... what the court must do is to place itself in thought in the same factual matrix as that in which the parties were. ... in the search for the relevant background, there may be facts which form part of the circumstances in which the parties contract in which one, or both, may take no particular interest, their minds being addressed to or concentrated on other facts so that if asked they would assert that they did not have these facts in the forefront of the mind, but that will not prevent those facts from forming part of an objective setting in which the contract is to be construed.'

Prenn v Simmonds (1971)

The court had to construe 'profits available for dividend'. The judgment, following Cardozo J, relied upon the commercial background of the objective aim of the transaction to give meaning to the phrase. It was held that the history of negotiations was not permissible to interpret the contract. Per Lord Wilberforce:

'In order for the agreement ... to be understood, it must be placed in its context. The time has long passed when agreements, even those under seal, were isolated from the matrix of facts in which they were set and interpreted purely on internal legalistic considerations .... We must enquire beyond the language and see what the circumstances were with reference to which the words were used, and the object, appearing from those circumstances, which the person using them had in view.'

The reason for excluding evidence of negotiations is

'... simply that such evidence is unhelpful. By the nature of things, where negotiations are difficult, the parties' positions, with each passing letter, are changing and until the final agreement, although converging, still divergent. It is only the final document which records a consensus. If the previous documents use different expressions, how does the construction of those expressions, itself a doubtful process, help on the construction of the contractual words? If the same expressions are used, nothing is gained by looking back; indeed something may be lost since the relevant surrounding circumstances may be different.'

VHE Construction Ltd v Alfred McAlpine Construction (1997)

The claimant subcontractors commenced discussion of contract terms on 4 January 1993 and started work on site three days later. Contract discussions were still ongoing in July 1993 when there were disagreements between the parties. HH Judge Bowsher decided on the facts that the parties had agreed the last outstanding term between them in late February or early March 1993 by telephone. The discussions thereafter were simply discussions about the terms that had already been agreed. Disputes raised at a later point could not be resolved by consideration of what was or was not said during negotiations nor by disputes raised after the making of the agreement, but by construction of the agreement as found by the court. Evidence of negotiations can be admitted for the purpose of identifying whether an agreement has been reached, but not for determination of its terms.

Bank of Scotland v Dunedin Property Investment Co Ltd (1998)

Per Lord Kirkwood:

'The court can have regard to "facts which both parties have had in mind and known that the other had in mind at the time when the contract was made".'

Investors Compensation Scheme Ltd v West Bromwich Building Society (1998)

This was an action against various building societies for compensation for breach of statutory duty. A preliminary issue arose as to construction of a clause of a claim form. Per Lord Hoffmann:

'The principles may be summarised as follows:

(1) Interpretation is the ascertainment of the meaning which the document would convey to a reasonable person having all the background knowledge which would reasonably have been available to the parties in the situation in which they were at the time of the contract.

(2) The background was famously referred to by Lord Wilberforce as the "matrix of fact", but this phrase is, if anything, an understated description of what the background may include. Subject to the requirement that it should have been reasonably available to the parties and to the exception to be mentioned next, it includes absolutely anything which would have affected the way in which the language of the document would have been understood by a reasonable man.

(3) The law excludes from the admissible background the previous negotiations of the parties and their declarations of subjective intent. They are admissible only in an action for rectification. The law makes this distinction for reasons of practical policy and, in this respect only, legal interpretation differs from the way we would interpret utterances in ordinary life. The boundaries of this exception are in some respects unclear. But this is not the occasion on which to explore them.

(4) The meaning which a document (or any other utterance) would convey to a reasonable man is not the same thing as the meaning of its words. The meaning of words is a matter of dictionaries and grammars; the meaning of the document is what the parties using those words against the relevant background would reasonably have been understood to mean. The background may not merely enable the reasonable man to choose between the possible meanings of words which are ambiguous but even (as occasionally happens in ordinary life) to conclude that the parties must, for whatever reason, have used the wrong words or syntax. …

(5) The "rule" that words should be given their "natural and ordinary meaning" reflects the commonsense proposition that we do not easily accept that people have made linguistic mistakes, particularly in formal documents. On the other hand, if one would nevertheless

conclude from the background that something must have gone wrong with the language, the law does not require judges to attribute to the parties an intention which they plainly could not have had.'

BCCI v Ali (2002)

Lord Hoffmann clarified what he meant by 'absolutely anything' in the second principle in *Investors Compensation Scheme* when considering the admissible background facts. He stated that:

'I did not think it necessary to emphasise that I meant anything which a reasonable man would have regarded as relevant. I was merely saying that there is no conceptual limit to what can be regarded as background. It is not, for example, confined to the factual background but can include the state of the law (as in cases in which one takes into account that the parties are unlikely to have intended to agree to something unlawful or legally ineffective) or proved common assumptions which were in fact quite mistaken ... I was certainly not encouraging a trawl through "background" which could not have made a reasonable person think that parties must have departed from conventional usage.'

He also confirmed that:

'... it would be contrary to basic principles of construction for the meaning of a document to be affected by facts which were known to one party but not reasonably available to the other.'

Howgate Shopping Centre v Catercraft Services Ltd (2004)

This case involved interpretation of a rent review provision in a sublease. Lord Macfadyen referred to case law and added, referring to the first of Lord Hoffmann's principles in *Investors Compensation Scheme*:

'In seeking to identify the background circumstances which may legitimately be taken into account in interpreting the rent review provisions of the sub-lease, I bear in mind that regard may be had only to circumstances knowledge of which was, or ought reasonably to have been, available to both parties. ...

The aspect of this matter which, in my view, presents a need for particular care is where the respective parties to a contract had differing degrees of knowledge about certain of the background circumstances.'

ProForce Recruit Ltd v Rugby Group Ltd (2007)

This case centred on the meaning of the words 'preferred supplier status' in a commercial agreement. This phrase had been used in pre-contractual correspondence but was not defined in the contract and a dispute arose over its meaning.

Cresswell J noted the judicial shift from the literal interpretation of contracts to a more commercial approach. He started by summarising the settled principles of contractual construction (*Investors Compensation Scheme v West Bromwich Building Society*). Words will be given their ordinary and natural meaning, and if contracting parties wish to give words a specific meaning (the 'agreed dictionary exception'), they should state that meaning in the contract itself. The problem here was that they had not done so. Hence, 'preferred' was interpreted as 'approved', i.e. the supplier was of a certain standing, but it did not mean exclusive, or that the supplier must be approached first. Rugby was not contractually committed to trading only with its 'preferred' suppliers. Neither was there any basis for implying a term to the effect suggested by ProForce.

The phrase had been used in pre-contractual discussions, but it was noted that although, exceptionally, evidence of such discussions may be admissible to show that the parties had agreed that certain words would bear a specific meaning, this exception 'will seldom arise in the interpretation of commercial contracts'.

Chartbrook Ltd v Persimmon Homes Ltd and others (2007)

The court determined that prior negotiations are not admissible except in limited cases, known as the 'private dictionary inroad', where evidence of negotiations showed the parties had agreed a particular meaning which had then been used in the contract without definition.

Drawing on *Investors Compensation Scheme*, the court concluded that the exclusion of negotiations from the admissible background facts when construing a contract was based on policy considerations. The court was also influenced by the need to protect third parties who might need to understand the contract, for example on assignment. If negotiations were admissible evidence, third parties would not be able to make safe assumptions about a contract's meaning without carrying out an enquiry into the negotiations that took place. The court therefore rejected the defendant's argument and upheld the bar on use of evidence of the parties' negotiations in construing a contract:

> '... there is a powerful need to preserve on policy grounds a rule which excludes the parties' negotiations from the admissible background when construing, rather than rectifying, a commercial contract.'

The court then considered the cases said to establish the 'private dictionary inroad' into this principle. Although it would have preferred to have no exceptions to the rule and to explain the cases as being concerned with rectification, the court felt bound by the Court of Appeal's earlier decision in *ProForce* to allow this exception: the exception should not, however, extend to a case in which the word, phrase, clause or term is expressly defined in the contract.

Commission for New Towns v Cooper (Great Britain) Ltd (1995)

The court considered the effect of an agreement made between a statutory body which had succeeded to the rights of Milton Keynes District Council, and a UK subsidiary of an American corporation. A representative of the American corporation had procured a local official to agree to grant to the UK subsidiary the right to surrender a lease without penalty in circumstances where it was clear that, although the terms of the agreement made did indeed include the right conferred, it had never been intended so to do. There was no ambiguity in the words used in the agreement; nor could it be said that there had been any actual misrepresentation. The American group, it was found, made a deliberate attempt to hide the other's mistake and that made the contract unenforceable.

The court, having looked at the negotiations, held that rectification could be granted to exclude the conferment of the option. In the course of doing so, Stewart-Smith LJ gave a remarkably wide statement of the law, noting that where A intends B to be mistaken as to the construction of a contract and diverts B's attention from discovering the mistake by making false and misleading statements, and B makes the mistake which A intends, then suspicion and not actual knowledge of the mistake is enough for rectification to be granted.

1.2 AGREEMENTS TO AGREE/NEGOTIATE

When parties commence work, it is not unusual for there to be some matters that are not agreed. If there is no agreement at all, work might be valued on a quantum meruit. The court will uphold an agreement that contains the essential elements, such as price and scope of work, but a period of time in which to do the work does not need to be agreed, as it is implied that the work will be completed in a reasonable time. Difficulties can also arise where the parties commence work, but they have agreed between them that details will be resolved at a future date. The House of Lords decided in *Walford v Miles* that an agreement between two parties that a matter is to be agreed between them at a future date – an 'agreement to agree' – is unenforceable under English law. An exception may arise where the element to be agreed is not an essential part of the contract. Where the obligation is to use best endeavours, the agreement will be upheld.

Two exceptions to this general rule are highlighted below. In the first case of *Alstom Signalling v Jarvis Facilities Ltd*, the court found that it could settle the points remaining as they were not essential terms. In *Petromec v Petroleo Brazileiro SA Petrobras*, the court examined the enforceability of a provision that was effectively an agreement to agree when included as a term in the enforceable contract. It was held that this category of case should be treated differently from *Walford*.

Walford v Miles (1992)

In 1992, the House of Lords had held that an agreement for consideration to deal exclusively with one potential contractor and to terminate any other negotiations then current with others lacked certainty and was unenforceable as being, in effect, a bare agreement to negotiate. The leading speech was by Lord Ackner, with whom the other Lords agreed, where he said:

> 'The reason why an agreement to negotiate, like an agreement to agree, is unenforceable is simply because it lacks the necessary certainty. The same does not apply to an agreement to use best endeavours. This uncertainty is demonstrated in the instant case by the provision which it is said has to be implied in the agreement for the determination of the negotiations. How can courts be expected to decide whether, *subjectively*, a proper reason existed for the termination of negotiations? The answer suggested depends upon whether the negotiations have been determined "in good faith". However, the concept of a duty to carry on negotiations in good faith is inherently repugnant to the adversarial position of the parties when involved in negotiations. Each party to the negotiations is entitled to pursue his (or her) own interest, so long as he avoids making misrepresentations. To advance that interest he must be entitled, if he thinks it is appropriate, to threaten to withdraw from further negotiations or to withdraw in fact, in the hope that the opposite party may seek to reopen negotiations by offering improved terms. Mr. Naughton, of course, accepts that the agreement upon which he relies does not contain a duty to complete the negotiations. But that still leaves the vital question – how is a vendor ever to know that he is entitled to withdraw from further negotiations? How is the court to police such an "agreement"? A duty to negotiate in good faith is as unworkable in practice as it is inherently inconsistent with the position of a negotiating party. It is here that the uncertainty lies. In my judgment, while negotiations are in existence either party is entitled to withdraw from these negotiations, at any time for any reason. There can be thus no obligation to continue to negotiate until there is "a proper reason" to withdraw. Accordingly, a bare agreement to negotiate has no legal content.'

Alstom Signalling v Jarvis Facilities Ltd (2004)

Alstom, the main contractor for the Tyne & Wear metro, engaged Jarvis. The subcontract was never signed. Under the draft subcontract the base price was agreed and there was to be a pain/gain share mechanism, but details of this were not resolved. Alstom suggested the mechanism reflect that in the main contract. Jarvis argued that this was no more than an agreement to agree and was unenforceable, following *Walford v Miles*. It was held that both parties undertook implied primary obligations to make reasonable endeavours to agree on the pain/gain provisions by which Jarvis would participate in some way in the main contract pain/gain mechanism. There was a difference, but the court was empowered to make a determination. Mr Recorder Colin Reese QC noted:

> 'Neither party could thwart the agreement by refusing to negotiate in good faith and/or by refusing to allow an Adjudicator or a TCC Judge to resolve the matter. It is implicit in the agreement that the standard by which the Adjudicator or TCC Judge is to be guided is fairness and reasonableness as between the parties. If each party has negotiated in good faith but neither has been persuaded to accept the other's view and there has been no compromise, the Adjudicator or Judge is the person who is entrusted to decide what would be a fair and reasonable mechanism which should apply. If one party refuses to negotiate, the other has an effective remedy because the Adjudicator or Judge can be invited to consider the facts/matters/arguments which it wishes to put forward, together with whatever facts/matters/arguments the previously reluctant party may elect to bring forward at that stage, before deciding what would be a fair and reasonable mechanism which should apply. Quite obviously, in performing such a task, the Adjudicator or Judge may have to choose between a number of possible solutions, each of which could be said to be fair and reasonable but, that is something which he (or she) has been specifically empowered to do by the parties.'

Mr Recorder Reese QC noted that the provisions in issue in this case related to subsidiary/non-essential questions; the procedure for calculation of the gain or pain is a matter of machinery and that the courts had a history of determining such points, before concluding:

'... I can see nothing to prevent the Court considering and resolving the difference or differences between these parties concerning the precise mechanism by which, in some meaningful way, Jarvis should participate in the scheme of gain sharing or pain sharing which was agreed as part of the Main Contract.'

Petromec v Petroleo Brazileiro SA Petrobras and Another (2004), (2005)

This dispute arose from an engineering contract. The court at first instance examined the enforceability of a clause that was included as a term in an enforceable contract. The clause provided that the parties would negotiate in good faith to reach agreement on certain amounts of costs for the upgrade of a semi-submersible oil production platform which were payable to one of the parties under a separate clause in the contract.

The court held that this type of situation was different from the pre-contract negotiations addressed in *Walford v Miles* but that, while the process remained one of negotiations, the fundamental objections still applied, as the ultimate object of the negotiations was to reach agreement and it would still be impossible to identify the content of such agreement. Such an agreement was not enforceable because of the uncertainty of the outcome of such negotiations. Even if an obligation to negotiate in good faith were recognised in cases where it forms part of an agreement, a breach of such obligation would not enable the innocent party to recover the benefit of the bargain to which the bona fide negotiations would have led, because the very existence of such bargain and its terms would always remain uncertain. However, the Court of Appeal (although dealing with the issue on an obiter basis) left room for change on this point and held that the fact that the obligation to negotiate in good faith is made part of a complex agreement is relevant, and 'it would be a strong thing to declare unenforceable a clause into which the parties have deliberately and expressly entered'. Longmore LJ concluded that *Walford v Miles* was not binding in relation to such an express obligation to negotiate.

1.3 FORMATION OF CONTRACT: EXISTENCE OF OFFER, ACCEPTANCE AND BATTLE OF FORMS

Construction contracts are often let following a series of events involving an invitation to tender, tender, tender amendments, negotiations, pre-start meeting, introduction of standard terms and contract award. Questions can arise, such as what terms govern the contract? What offer or counter-offer contains the terms that are binding on the parties? At what point was the contract formed? In resolving these difficulties the courts have often adopted what has been called the 'last shot principle' as established in the case of *Butler Machine Tool Co v Ex-Cell-O-Corp*. In other words, the courts may look at the last offer which had been accepted without qualification, and this would then determine the conditions of contract.

Some illustration of the difficulties with application of *Butler* is evident from *Balmoral Group Ltd v Borealis (UK) Ltd* and *Sterling Hydraulics Ltd v Dichtomatick Ltd*. Both cases involved a supplier and issues as to whether either party could rely upon standard terms of business as having being incorporated within the agreement.

The recent decision in *Cubitt Building & Interiors Ltd v Richardson Roofing (Industrial) Ltd* shows the confusion that can arise as to when a contract is formed. This case emphasised the importance of pre-contract meeting minutes, indicating that in some instances these may be sufficient to constitute a contract. The refusal to execute a subcontract order does not necessarily mean there is no contract in place, as it may have already been formed.

Other cases have noted difficulties with incorporation of standard terms of business. In situations where both parties purport to impose their own standard terms, difficulties arise in determining which terms will prevail. The approach which has been taken by the courts is that an acceptance of terms which itself imposes new terms does not amount to an acceptance, but is a counter-offer which is capable of being accepted by the other party. This has meant that generally the last set of terms before acceptance or performance of the contract prevails. These cases establish that there is no set rule for determining the battle of the forms, and the last shot fired in the battle of the forms will not necessarily prevail.

As noted in *Cubitt*, parties should not underestimate the importance of pre-start meeting minutes and should not assume that, because a letter refers to a formal contract being entered into, there is no contract for the time being. *Rackline Ltd v The National Library of Wales* highlights the confusion that can arise when a supplier deals first with the employer but where, in the event that an agreement cannot be reached, the supplier deals with the main contractor at a later stage. The argument is raised that a binding contract for the works had in any event been formed at an earlier stage.

In *Pagnan SpA v Feed Products Ltd*, the court set out the principles to be followed in determining whether an agreement has been formed. The essential elements required for an agreement were discussed in *Courtney and Fairbairn Ltd v Tolaini Brothers (Hotels) Ltd*. Even where it is clear that the parties have formed an agreement, but done so several months after work has started on site, the decision in *Trollope & Colls v Atomic Power Constructions* confirmed in that case that the contract's provisions govern retrospectively to the commencement of the works.

Finally, one of the more difficult points arising with the interpretation of subcontracts concerns the extent to which another party's terms, or third party provisions, are incorporated by reference. In *Tradigrain SA v King Diamond Shipping SA (The 'Spiros C')*, the general principles are set out, points which have now been adopted in other cases by the High Court in England.

Butler Machine Tool Co Ltd v Ex-Cell-O Corp (England) Ltd (1979)

Butler provided a quotation for machine tools. Its standard terms were printed on the reverse side, with a price variation clause and with a note that these terms should prevail. Ex-Cell-O placed an order subject to its standard terms, without any price escalation clause, at the foot of which was a tear-off acknowledgement of order slip. Butler signed and returned the slip under cover of a letter that referred to Butler's original quotation. In a claim by Butler to recover the price with price escalation, there was an issue as to whose terms prevailed or what the terms of the agreement were.

The Court of Appeal found for Ex-Cell-O. Lord Denning MR said that the documents have to be considered as a whole, and thought that the acknowledgement of order was the decisive document, as it made clear that the contract was on Ex-Cell-O's terms and did not include price variation, adding:

> 'In some cases the battle is won by the man who fires the last shot. He is the man who puts forward the latest terms and conditions: and, if they are not objected to by the other party, he may be taken to have agreed to them .... In some cases, however, the battle is won by the man who gets the blow in first. If he offers to sell at a named price on the term and conditions [sic] stated on the back and the buyer orders the goods purporting to accept the offer on an order form with his own different terms and conditions on the back, then, if the difference is so material that it would affect the price, the buyer ought not to be allowed to take advantage of the difference unless he draws it specifically to the attention of the seller ... conflicting terms may have to be scrapped and replaced by a reasonable implication.'

Balmoral Group Ltd v Borealis (UK) Ltd (2006)

In this case, the seller, Borealis, gave a written quotation which said that sales were 'subject to normal terms and current conditions of sale'. Balmoral did not ask what the terms were and placed its order. Subsequently invoices which contained various exclusion clauses were sent by Borealis which Balmoral did not read but signed for payment. Some months later, Balmoral submitted another order but with a stamped reference to its own terms which required compliance with Sale of Goods legislation, such legislation being the subject of Borealis' exclusion clauses. A dispute arose over the quality of the goods supplied. On the facts of this case, the 'last form filed' argument was rejected. It was found that Balmoral had never produced a copy of its own conditions in full, nor mentioned the change in terms.

Sterling Hydraulics Ltd v Dichtomatick Ltd (2007)

The buyer's order form requested supply 'subject to the terms and conditions set out below and overleaf'. The seller's faxed acknowledgment of order was printed by computer on two blank sheets, one containing its letterhead and conditions of payment and the other nothing more than the statement 'delivery based on our General Terms of Sale'. In subsequent invoices, the same message was relayed, although a few stated the seller's terms on the reverse. A dispute arose and the seller denied liability on the basis of its standard terms. The court found that the buyer knew that the seller had its own terms but could not be seen to have read or understood them, nor to have agreed to them.

Cubitt and Interiors Ltd v Richardson Roofing (Industrial) Ltd (2008)

Cubitt was the main contractor on a mixed residential and commercial scheme. Richardson was a specialist roofing contractor who was invited to quote for the roofing works on the project. Various documents were exchanged by the parties and the question arose whether Cubitt's standard terms and conditions had been incorporated in the contract or the standard form of DOM/1 applied.

Contrary to what each party was arguing, the judge found that the contract had actually been formed at the pre-contract meeting when 'substantial agreement on every aspect of the subcontract was reached' and recorded in the minutes of the meeting. The judge decided that prior to the letter of intent being issued there was an offer capable of acceptance – the final revised price together with all the items agreed at the meeting. This letter of intent was Cubitt's acceptance of that offer. It did not matter that there was an intention to enter into a formal contract in the future. He came to this conclusion despite the fact that Cubitt subsequently sent what it purported to be a letter of intent and referred to the entering into of a formal subcontract.

With respect to the 'battle of the forms', the judge concluded that although Cubitt's subsequent order referred to its own standard terms and conditions, these were never in fact provided to Richardson. Furthermore, the reference to the DOM/1 form of contract in all other documents implied that this form of subcontract had been agreed by both parties.

(See also section 3.1 on letters of intent/award/ appointment.)

Rackline Ltd v The National Library of Wales (1999)

Rackline provided tenders for the design, supply and maintenance of shelving. It was awarded the design contract but was unable to form a supply subcontract later with the main contractor. It claimed that acceptance of the design contract also meant that it had been awarded the other contracts direct with the employer at an earlier stage. The claim failed. In the Court of Appeal, Lord Justice Tuckey said:

> 'The fact that both parties intended that Rackline should get the sub-contract is not enough. An intention to contract does not create a contract, still less an intention that someone else should contract. It does not follow that because Rackline were required to enter into the sub-contract if their tender was accepted the Library must have agreed to require the main contractor to do likewise. The promise that the main contractor would award the sub-contract within seven days of the main contact was not a promise that it would be awarded to Rackline. It simply ensured that the sub-contract would be awarded promptly.'

Pagnan SpA v Feed Products Ltd (1987)

The issue was whether there was a concluded contract for the sale and purchase of corn pellets by American sellers to Italian buyers. Lloyd LJ, with whom Stocker and O'Connor LJJ agreed, set out some propositions of law:

'(1) In order to determine whether a contract has been concluded in the course of correspondence, one must first look to the correspondence as a whole. ...

(2) Even if the parties have reached agreement on all the terms of the proposed contract, nevertheless they may intend that the contract shall not become binding until some further condition has been fulfilled. That is the ordinary "subject to contract" case.

(3) Alternatively, they may intend that the contract shall not become binding until some further term or terms have been agreed ... .

(4) Conversely, the parties may intend to be bound forthwith even though there are further terms still to be agreed or some further formality to be fulfilled ... .

(5) If the parties fail to reach agreement on such further terms, the existing contract is not invalidated unless the failure to reach agreement on such further terms renders the contract as a whole unworkable or void for uncertainty.

(6) It is sometimes said that the parties must agree on essential terms and that it is only matters of detail which can be left over. This may be misleading, since the word "essential" in that context is ambiguous. If by "essential" one means a term without which the contract cannot be enforced, then the statement is true: the law cannot enforce an incomplete contract. If by "essential" one means a term which the parties have agreed to be essential for the formation of a binding contract, then the statement is tautologous. If by "essential" one means only a term which the Court regards as important as opposed to a term which the Court regards as less important or a matter of detail, the statement is untrue. It is for the parties to decide whether they wish to be bound and, if so, by what terms, whether important or unimportant. It is the parties who are, in the memorable phrase coined by the Judge, "the masters of their contractual fate". Of course the more important the term the less likely it is that the parties will have left it for future decision. But there is no legal obstacle which stands in the way of the parties agreeing to be bound now while deferring important matters to be agreed later. It happens every day when parties enter into so-called "heads of agreement".'

The Court of Appeal was upholding a decision that a contract had been formed and Lloyd LJ was therefore, in his proposition 6, particularly concerned to emphasise that the court cannot make 'essential' a term which the parties regarded as inessential. The Court of Appeal fully accepted the converse principle that there is no contract if the parties are not in agreement on what they regard as an essential term. And '[of] course the more important the term the less likely it is that the parties will have left it for future decision'.

Trollope & Colls v Atomic Power Constructions (1963)

The claimant subcontractor submitted a tender and started work on site in June 1959. The agreement was not fully agreed and signed until April 1960. Variations had arisen in the intervening period. An issue arose as to whether there was a contract governing the parties' rights as to work done since June 1959. It was held that there was no principle of English law which provides that a contract cannot have retrospective effect, or that if it purported to have such effect it would be a nullity. Here, it was necessary to give business efficacy to the contract such that the variation clauses would apply retrospectively.

Courtney and Fairbairn Ltd v Tolaini Brothers (Hotels) Ltd (1975)

The defendants, who sought to develop a site, discussed plans with the plaintiff contractor about provision of finance and acting as contractor. They offered, if the introduction of finance was acceptable, 'to negotiate fair and reasonable sums' for the project, based upon agreed estimates of cost and a 5 per cent profit margin. The defendants agreed to 'the terms specified'. Finance was introduced, but after differences over building prices, another contractor was engaged. The plaintiffs sought damages for breach and claimed a reasonable sum for services rendered. The first instance decision for the contractor was reversed on appeal. Per Lord Denning MR:

> 'Now the price in a building contract is of fundamental importance. It is so essential a term that there is no contract unless the price is agreed or there is an agreed method of ascertaining it, not dependent on the negotiations of the two parties themselves. ...

> In the absence of some such machinery, the only contract which you might find is a contract to do the work for a reasonable sum, or a sum to be fixed by a third party. But here there is no contract at all. ...

> If the law does not recognise a contract to enter into a contract (when there is a fundamental term yet to be agreed) it seems to me it cannot recognise a contract to negotiate. The reason is because it is too uncertain to have any binding force.'

Tradigrain SA v King Diamond Shipping SA (The 'Spiros C') (2000)

On questions of construction where one document's terms

are incorporated into another document, it was decided that there were two rules. The first is to construe the incorporating clause in order to decide on the width of the incorporation. The second 'is to read the incorporated wording into the host document in extenso to see if, in that setting, some parts of the incorporated wording nevertheless have to be rejected as inconsistent or insensible when read in their new context'. This second rule broadly reflects the judgment of Buckley LJ in *Modern Building (Wales) Ltd v Limmer and Trinidad Co Ltd*.

Rix LJ stated:

'Where parties by an agreement import the terms of some other document as part of their agreement those terms must be imported in their entirety, in my judgment, but subject to this: that if any of the imported terms in any way conflict with the expressly agreed terms, the latter must prevail over what would otherwise be imported.'

In the case of such conflict, the provisions of the incorporating document prevail and parts of the incorporated document are rejected.

1.4 ADVICE AND SELECTION OF CONTRACTS

Errors in advice and selection of contract forms can have serious implications, most obviously for the owner, who will expect his interests to be properly protected. In *Bramall & Ogden v Sheffield City Council*, the effect of utilising a form of contract without provision for sectional completion was to deprive the owner of the right to deduct liquidated damages for delay. It is clear from *Kenny & Reynolds v Pyper* that a consultant who produced an unsuitable contract, having failed to exclude from specification for cost purposes an item deleted from the design, could be liable in negligence (although on the facts the defendant architect was able to escape liability in that case).

It is not the law that there is a single correct contract choice for every project, omission to find which would constitute negligence. HH Judge Coulson (as he then was) in *Cunningham v Collett & Farmer* accepted that different consultants might legitimately prefer different standard forms, so that it would not be negligent to recommend the *JCT Minor*

Works contract for its clarity and simplicity even though the contract sum was above the recommended guide figure. Nor would it be wrong to proceed by way of a letter of intent, even though the device is often used inappropriately (see 3.1 on letters of intent), provided the conditions justifying the decision are met; the *Cunningham* case provides invaluable guidance to clients and their professional advisers in this respect.

However, Judge Coulson did not say that there is complete freedom of choice in advising on selection of a procurement method or form of contract: that freedom applied 'unless there is a very good reason why he should not use it in a particular instance'. That important proviso means that consultants and others involved in advice and decision-making on procurement process will have to consider appropriateness in every case, notwithstanding that they can properly fall back on their favoured form or method where there are other eligible choices.

Plymouth and South West Co-operative Society v Architecture Structure & Management is a salutary example of the need for 'considered discussion' of the method of procurement, especially where, as in that case, the client had well established priorities, in that case for strict budgetary control. The decision to adopt an otherwise respected procurement method like the two-stage tendering process could still constitute negligence on the part of the advisor if it failed to take account of the client's requirements.

Kenny & Reynolds Ltd v Pyper (1964)

An architect failed to delete from the specifications a percentage sum allocated for a central heating system after the decision had been taken to exclude the item from the scope of works. The court held this to be inexcusable and to constitute professional negligence, but the architect avoided the consequences of his error because the client was taken, on the facts, to have signed the building contract with knowledge of the error.

Bramall & Ogden Ltd v Sheffield City Council (1985)

The council was held not to be entitled to deduct liquidated and ascertained damages (under *JCT 63 Local Authorities*

Edition) in a situation where it had taken over houses as they were completed by the contractor. This was because a contract had been mistakenly selected which did not make provision for sectional completion, so that the liquidated damages provisions would become penal and thus unenforceable. Case law and the leading text *Keating on Building Contracts* (4th edition) had stated clearly that express provision was necessary, and during the course of the project itself the JCT had issued a sectional completion supplement together with a practice note to meet this need. However, the parties had not amended the contract chosen. As the judge concluded:

> 'It would of course be open to the parties to have made appropriate provision in the contract itself so as to deal with the situation. ... in the absence of any provision for sectional completion in this contract, the respondents were not entitled to claim or deduct liquidated damages ... .'

Cunningham v Collett & Farmer (2007)

The claimants, the owners, alleged that the defendant architects had been negligent in advising the use of the then current edition of the *JCT Minor Works* (MW) contract for use on the refurbishment of a large Georgian mansion. The JCT guidance notes suggested that the MW form was suitable (in 2002) for works with a value up to £100,000, whereas the owners' budget was £500,000 and the lowest tender over £600,000. The judge held that there was 'nothing intrinsically wrong with the choice of MW 98 for the project' and that he had 'always regarded the comparative brevity of the Minor Works form, and the clarity of its terms, as giving it a major advantage over a number of other, rather more prolix standard forms of building contract issued by the JCT'. Overall,

> 'The recommendation of which standard form of building contract should be used for a particular project will usually come down to the consultant's personal preference and his previous experience. Such a subjective basis for choice seems to me to be entirely reasonable: if, as a contract administrator, a professional person likes and understands the way a particular standard form works, then, unless there is a very good reason why he should not use it in a

particular instance, it seems to be to everybody's advantage if he recommends that form for use on his projects.'

The judge also rejected the claimant's criticism that there were insufficient tenderers: in the circumstances 'the defendants acted quite properly in seeking five, and ending up with three, prospective tenderers'.

The claimants had also alleged that the defendant architects had been negligent in utilising a letter of intent. HH Judge Coulson distinguished between two types of letter of intent. The first type, the letter of intent 'properly so-called, is a document which expresses an intention on the part of party A to enter into a contract in the future with party B, but creates no liability in regard to that future contract. It is expressly designed to have no binding effect whatsoever'. By contrast, the second type, the commonest in the modern construction industry, are 'expressly designed to give rise to some, albeit limited, reciprocal rights and liabilities'.

It was the second type which had been utilised in this case. The judge saw the main problem with such letters of intent as a practical one:

'... once they have been sent, and the contractor has started work pursuant to that letter of intent, all those involved, including the professional team, can easily take their eye off the ball and forget about the importance of ensuring that the full contract documents are signed as quickly as possible. ... very often, something goes wrong on site and, in the absence of a full contract to regulate the parties' rights and obligations in such circumstances, the result is confusion and acrimony.'

He criticised the use of the letters of intent 'issued in the hope that, once the work is underway, potentially difficult contract issues will somehow resolve themselves. They are plainly not appropriate in such circumstances'.

However, he did not agree that the letters of intent are, as a matter of principle, almost always inappropriate: 'There will be times when a letter of intent is the best way of ensuring that the works can start promptly, with a clear timetable both for the finalisation of the contract formalities, and for the carrying out of the works themselves.'

The judge gave guidance on when a letter of intent might properly be used, i.e. where:

(i)   the contract workscope and the price are either agreed or there is a clear mechanism for their agreement;

(ii)   the contract terms are, or are very likely to be, agreed;

(iii)   the start and finish dates and contract programme are broadly agreed;

(iv)   there are good reasons to start work in advance of the finalisation of all contract documents.

In the result, the use of the letter of intent was not negligent on the part of the defendant architects.

(See also section 3.1 on letters of intent.)

Plymouth and South West Co-operative Society v Architecture Structure & Management Ltd (2007)

The court held that the two-stage tendering procedure adopted for the re-development of the Co-op's flagship store in Plymouth was inappropriate for the project. The court noted the content of the *NJCC Code of Procedure for Two Stage Selective Tendering* (1994 edition) to the effect that

> '... the purpose of the two-stage tendering procedure is to accelerate the date when a project can be started on site where a delay in completing the design drawings is envisaged, particularly where a potential contractor can assist in the completion of the design stage and in keeping costs down by advising on ways that the project can be implemented that will save time and money.'

The disadvantage in the context of this project was that most of the decision-making and programming would have to be completed well before the second stage. The court was critical of the fact that 'there was no considered discussion' about the method of procurement, given the client's need for strict budgetary control. The high proportion of provisional sum work in the contract would virtually ensure that the sums payable to the contractor would increase. The defendant architects were held to have been negligent and in breach of their duty to their clients in not discussing alternative strategies, whereby different phasing of the construction could have been coupled with a different procurement method.

1.5 FORMALITIES AND THE NEED FOR WRITTEN AGREEMENTS

The *Housing Grants, Construction and Regeneration Act* 1996 provides parties to a construction contract a right to refer disputes to adjudication. That is limited to certain defined categories of construction contract and to contracts 'in writing'. There have been a number of decisions of courts in England as to whether particular contracts fall within that category. The first decision, *RJT Consulting Engineers Ltd v DM Engineering (Northern Ireland) Ltd*, was a case in which engineers had agreed to carry out work orally; there were other documents (such as invoices) that confirmed the existence of the agreement, but that argument was lost. In the second case, *Mast Electrical Services v Kendall Cross Holdings Ltd*, there were numerous quotations provided but it was not clear which was agreed. In that case, there was evidence in writing, but it was not evidence of what had been agreed. These cases confirm that the aim of the statute was that there would be no contention with respect to contract terms with which the adjudicator would have to decide. That may be changed as a result of the revisions to the Act being undertaken by Parliament at the time of writing.

RJT Consulting Engineers Ltd v DM Engineering (Northern Ireland) Ltd (2002)

The claimant engineers agreed orally to carry out engineering consultancy services. Disputes arising from the consultancy work were referred to adjudication pursuant to the *Housing Grants, Construction and Regeneration Act* 1996. The claimant challenged the defendant's right to refer the dispute to adjudication as, under section 107(1), the Act only applied where a construction contract was 'in writing'. In the Court of Appeal, Ward LJ noted that there were many documents recording the existence of an agreement, but that was insufficient. These were not evidence of the terms of the oral agreement. Per Auld LJ:

'What is important is that the terms of the agreement material to the issue or issues giving rise to the reference should be clearly recorded in writing, not that every term, however trivial or unrelated to those issues, should be expressly recorded or incorporated by reference.'

Mast Electrical Services v Kendall Cross Holdings Ltd (2007)

The claimant subcontractor provided a number of quotations for refurbishment projects, followed by revised quotations after surveys. Each quotation had different rates and prices. After work commenced, there was a dispute as to what rates applied. Jackson J held that the documents had not set out, evidenced or recorded all material terms of the claimant's subcontract work, particularly the agreed rates of payment between the parties. Accordingly, following *RJT Consulting Engineers*, there was no agreement 'in writing' to satisfy section 107 of the *Housing Grants, Construction and Regeneration Act* 1996.

2
Tender process

In considering the legal constraints on the tender process, it is necessary to make two distinctions, which are related. First, the constraints may be contractual or they may derive from regulation, although the latter may influence the content of the former. Second, the position will very often differ as between contracts in the private sector and the public sector. It is chiefly in the latter that the EU-inspired regulatory regimes apply, although contracts by utilities, such as water companies, could also be governed by regulation.

For many years, in English law, it seems to have been assumed that a tenderer had no legal protection unless and until the point was reached where a successful bid led to the entering into of the contract. Owners either actually were, or considered themselves, able to specify any tendering procedure and follow it or not as they chose, decide according to any objective criteria, or none, and treat the tenderers as equally or unequally as they wished.

This section traces the transformation of that position through the case law, which in English law spans the last three decades. Initially, this was entirely done through the device of the tender contract.

2.1 DEVELOPMENT OF TENDER CONTRACT

Tender contracts were well established in other common law jurisdictions well before they came to be developed in English law. *The Queen in Right of Ontario v Ron Engineering and Construction (Eastern) Ltd* was decided by the Supreme Court of Canada in the early 1980s, to the effect that submission of a conforming tender by a contractor resulted in the formation of a tender contract with the owner.

27

The first reported English construction case to apply this analysis was *Blackpool and Fylde Aero Club v Blackpool BC*, in which a conforming tenderer was held to be *contractually* entitled to have its tender considered with other conforming tenders. This was confirmed at about the same time (the dates of the publication of the reports give a misleading impression of the sequence of the decisions) by the Court of Appeal in *Fairclough Building Ltd v Port Talbot BC*, although that case emphasised that there might still be valid grounds for not considering the tender, such as breach of the rules of natural justice, despite the existence of the tender contract.

The Queen in Right of Ontario v Ron Engineering and Construction (Eastern) Ltd (1981)

Ron, the contractors, lodged a $150,000 tender deposit with their tender as required by the tender conditions, which provided for forfeiture in the event of failure to execute a contract after acceptance. Ron's tender was the lowest of eight, but within an hour of the opening of the tenders, the contractors found an error in their pricing. They requested to be allowed to withdraw or alternatively argued that their tender was incapable of acceptance, refusing to sign the contract documents at the tendered price. The Supreme Court of Canada held that, by submitting a conforming tender, Ron had entered into a tender contract with the client, the Government. In this case, the contract imposed certain obligations on the tenderer in the event of its tender succeeding, which Ron had failed to fulfil. As Estey J put it: 'This contract is brought into being automatically upon the submission of a tender.' It is thus a unilateral contract, where the offer is accepted by the doing of an act. One of the terms of the tender contract was that the deposit would be forfeited in the event of non-compliance by the successful tenderer with its obligation to enter into the principal contract at the agreed price.

Many of the subsequent tender contract cases focus on the rights of the tenderer and the obligations of the owner, and some of these even refer to *R v Ron Engineering*, which establishes the existence of a tender contract, even though breach here was by the contractor.

Blackpool and Fylde Aero Club v Blackpool BC (1990)

The Club's tender for a contract for a pleasure flying concession was submitted within the Council's deadline for tenders but was mistakenly marked 'late' and was therefore not considered. The Club claimed damages both in breach of contract and negligence, which were awarded by the first instance judge on the ground that the Council's request for tenders gave rise to an implied obligation on it to consider valid tenders received within the time limit. The Court of Appeal dismissed the Council's appeal and its judgment is regarded as an important early landmark in the development of 'tender contracts'. Bingham LJ gave a classic statement of the traditionally strong position of the tendering authority (the Council):

> 'A tendering procedure of this kind is, in many respects, heavily weighted in favour of the invitor. He can invite tenders from as many or as few parties as he chooses. He need not tell any of them who else or how many others, he has invited. The invitee may often, although not here, be put to considerable labour and expense in preparing a tender, ordinarily without recompense if he is unsuccessful. The invitation to tender may itself, in a complex case, although again not here, involve time and expense to prepare, but the invitor does not commit himself to proceed with the project, whatever it is; he need not accept the highest tender; he need not accept any tender; he need not give reasons to justify his acceptance or rejection of any tender received.'

However, and crucially:

> 'The invitee is in my judgment protected at least to this extent: if he submits a conforming tender before the deadline he is entitled, *not as a matter of mere expectation but of contractual right*, to be sure that his tender will after the deadline be opened and considered in conjunction with all other conforming tenders or at least that his tender will be considered if others are.' (Emphasis added.)

Fairclough Building Ltd v Port Talbot BC (1993)

Fairclough was removed from a short-list of tenderers by the Council on the ground that the Council's Principal Architect was married to one of Fairclough's directors. Fairclough argued that this was breach of the tender contract formed when it had submitted a conforming tender, as in *Blackpool and Fylde Aero Club v Blackpool BC* (see above). Fairclough's action was dismissed by the trial judge and its appeal rejected by the Court of Appeal. The trial judge had held that it was the duty of the Council 'honestly to consider the tenders of those whom they had placed on the shortlist, unless there were reasonable grounds for not doing so'. In these circumstances, where the rules of natural justice constrained the Council's scope for action: 'The defendants acted reasonably in removing the plaintiffs from the shortlist.' Lord Justice Parker in the Court of Appeal held that:

> 'There is nothing in that judgment which in my view conflicts with the judgment in the *Blackpool* case. Here was a case where consideration had begun. A situation had arisen which clearly called for consideration by the Council and they considered it.'

Blackpool and Fylde Aero Club Ltd v Blackpool Borough Council distinguished.

2.2 CONTENTS OF TENDER CONTRACT

The *Blackpool and Fylde Aero Club* case (see above) gave only a rudimentary statement of what might be the contractual rights and obligations of the parties to a tendering contract. Subsequent case law has provided further consideration and amplification of the contents of a tender contract.

As with the initial development of the tender contract, other common law jurisdictions have often been in advance of English law. Thus in *Pratt Contractors v Palmerston North City Council,* the New Zealand Court found the tender contract to comprise an obligation of fairness/good faith upon the owner, breached by unequal treatment of tenderers.

Harmon CFEM Facades UK Ltd v The Corporate Officer of the House of Commons is regarded as a landmark case in English law in this respect. The court, citing the *Blackpool and Fylde Aero Club* and *Fairclough* cases, stated a general contractual duty to consider all compliant tenders fairly, which had been breached in a number of ways. It must be observed that the judge was specifically referring to tendering in the public sector and that this was a contract covered by the *Public Works Contracts Regulations* 1991 ('the Regulations'). The Regulations could both inform the contents of the tender contract and provide statutory definitions of rights/obligations and a remedy in the event of breach.

Since the *Harmon* case, there have been further important considerations of obligations of the owner towards a contractor submitting a valid tender, under a tender contract. The Privy Council's consideration of the contents of a tender contract in *Pratt Contractors Ltd v Transit New Zealand*, on appeal from the New Zealand Court of Appeal, is reckoned by most commentators to represent both the law of England and New Zealand. The Privy Council considered further the duty to act fairly and equally, but also took the opportunity to state what would *not* be included, specifically in the obligations regarding the composition and operation of the Tender Evaluation Team. The Privy Council set some boundaries to the contents of the tender contract in this decision, as well as re-affirming the basic concept.

Most recently, two Northern Ireland cases have added to the body of law on the contents of tender contracts outside of statutory regulation. It has been observed above that the *Harmon* decision was expressly influenced by the application of the *Public Works Contracts Regulations* 1991. *Scott v Belfast Education & Library Board*, although a public sector case, concerned a project the value of which fell below the threshold for the application of the public procurement regime. It is significant for the judge's exploration of the meaning of fairness within a tender contract, and also because it was found that a mistake in the tender documents which could affect different tenderers unequally could constitute a breach of the tender contract duty of fairness.

There are comparatively few reported decisions concerning challenges to tendering exercises in the private sector. *J&A Developments Ltd v Edina Manufacturing Ltd*, applying the *Blackpool and Fylde Aero Club* and *Fairclough* cases, confirms that tender contracts can arise in the procurement of private sector projects in the same way as in the public sector cases, albeit that the content of the obligations, uninfluenced by statutory regulation, will often not be the same. However, if, as in *Edina*, a tendering procedure is specified, it will be a term of the tendering contract that it shall be observed and departure from the procedure will prima facie be a breach of the owner's tender contract obligations.

Pratt Contractors v Palmerston North City Council (1995)

The contractors successfully brought an action against the Council for breach of contract, the importance of the case being that it is an early tendering contract decision. The contractors had submitted the lowest of four conforming tenders, but the contract (for a flyover interchange) was awarded to a tenderer who had submitted an alternative tender as well, offering savings based on an alternative design. The successful tenderer offered to 'meet and discuss' the alternative with the Council. Gallen J held that this came 'close to negotiating with one of the tenderers within the tender process, but not on terms which apply to other tenderers'. While the tender contract between the Council and each conforming tenderer did not require acceptance of the lowest bid, it did comprise an obligation of fairness/good faith upon the Council and this had been breached by the Council's unequal and unfair treatment of the tenderers. The contractors were successful in recovering damages for wasted tender costs and for lost profit on the contract itself, but were unsuccessful in claiming lost profit on future contracts which could have been won by establishing a track-record in this kind of work; this head of damages was too speculative.

(Note: See also the unsuccessful action by Pratt Contractors in *Pratt Contractors v Transit New Zealand* below, on different facts.)

Harmon CFEM Facades (UK) Ltd v The Corporate Officer of the House of Commons (1999)

Harmon was the unsuccessful tenderer for the fenestration contract for a new Parliamentary building in Westminster, Portcullis House. It successfully sued the client in respect of breach of the tender contract and of the *Public Works Contracts Regulations* 1991 in letting the contract to a rival contractor whose tender had been higher. The court (the Technology and Construction Court) found that the Regulations had been breached by the use of the expression 'overall value for money' without further detail, which obliged the client to award the contract on price alone. The client had also breached its obligations in operating a covert 'Buy British' policy, which had disadvantaged the French-owned Harmon. The judge held that:

> '... it is not clear in English law that in the public sector where competitive tenders are sought and responded to, a contract comes into existence whereby the prospective employer impliedly agreed to consider all tenderers fairly.' (See the *Blackpool* and *Fairclough* cases.)

The client had not been fair in engaging in post-tender negotiations with the successful tenderer and in making certain procedural concessions to it alone. It was a further breach of the Regulations to fail to give all the reasons for the decision at the time of notification to Harmon, and reasons given subsequently could not be relied on. As a consequence of these breaches, Harmon was allowed to recover its tender costs. The damages could also include its profit, which could take account of the 'intra-group margin' deriving from Harmon's advantageous position in a group of companies.

(See *Harmon CFEM v Corporate Officer of the House of Commons (No. 2)* on quantum. See also section 5.1 on this case.)

Pratt Contractors Ltd v Transit New Zealand (2004)

Pratt Contractors had been unsuccessful in a tender for a highways contract in New Zealand despite receiving only a slightly lower score from Transit New Zealand's Tender Evaluation Team (TET) than the successful tenderers. The difference largely arose from evidence from a member of the TET who had previously worked with Pratt and raised doubts concerning its record of delayed completions and aggressive claims.

Pratt claimed damages for breach of its tender contract with Transit. The case came to the Privy Council from the New Zealand Court of Appeal. The Privy Council agreed that there was an implied obligation on Transit to act fairly. Lord Hoffmann said that the duty:

> '... required that the evaluation ought to express the views honestly held by the members of the TET. The duty to act

fairly meant that all the tenderers had to be treated equally. One tenderer could not be given a higher mark than another if their attributes were the same.'

However,

'... Transit was not obliged to give tenderers the same mark if it honestly thought that their attributes were different. Nor did the duty of fairness mean that Transit were obliged to appoint people who came to the task without any views about the tenderers, whether favourable or adverse. ... The obligation of good faith and fair dealing also did not mean that the TET had to act judicially. It did not have to accord Mr Pratt a hearing or enter into debate with him ... . It would no doubt have been bad faith for a member of the TET to take steps to avoid receiving information because he strongly suspected that it might show that his opinion on some point was wrong. But that is all.'

The contractor's appeal was dismissed.

Gerard Martin Scott v Belfast Education & Library Board (2007)

In a preliminary hearing, clarification was sought as to whether tender documents give rise to an implied contractual term of fairness and good faith. The judge, in the Northern Ireland Chancery Division, declared himself 'satisfied that an implied contract can arise from the submission of a tender. It may arise by inference from the scheme of the tendering process and the presumed intention of the parties'. This could be so even though it was a public sector contract below the threshold for the application of the Public Procurement Rules.

The judge held that it would be an implied term that the employer will act fairly and in good faith, in the following respects:

'(1) Fairness applies to the nature and application of the specified procedures in a particular contract.

(2) Fairness applies to the assessment of the tenders according to the stated criteria.

(3) Fairness applies to the evaluation of the tenders in a uniform manner and as intended by the tender documents.'

The second question decided by the judge was that a mistake in the tender documents could affect different tenderers unequally and could thus constitute breach of the duty of fairness. An ambiguity could also affect the uniformity of evaluation.

(See also section 1.2 on good faith.)

J&A Developments Ltd v Edina Manufacturing Ltd (2007)

Six contractors tendered for an industrial project in Northern Ireland; the conditions of tender included the Code of Procedure for Single Stage Selective Tendering. The client called the three lowest tenderers to a meeting and requested that they reduce their tenders. The lowest tenderer, J&A Developments, refused and was not awarded the contract when the second lowest tenderer reduced its price. J&A brought an action against the client for breach of contract. The court gave judgment for J&A, starting from the proposition that 'a collateral contract can exist between a tenderer and an employer' based on *Blackpool and Fylde Aero Club v Blackpool BC*.

The Code of Procedure contained the principle that:

> '... it is a deplorable practice to seek to reduce any tender arbitrarily where the tender has been submitted in free competition and no modifications to the specification quantity or conditions under which the work is to be executed are to be made or to reduce tenders other than the lowest to a figure below the lowest tender.'

The Code was clearly incorporated expressly into the conditions of tender. The court's conclusion was:

> '... that there was a binding contract to the effect the principles of the Code would be applied and that therefore while there was no obligation on the defendants to accept the lowest tender they bound themselves to accept either no tender at all of those submitted or one at the price at which it was submitted subject to the possibility of reduction in circumstance contemplated by the Code.'

Nolan L J had said in *Fairclough Building v Port Talbot BC* that:

'... provided that the ground of rejection does not conflict with some binding undertaking or representation previously given by the customer to the tenderer the latter cannot complain.'

The court applied this in concluding that:

'... a binding undertaking or representation was given by the defendants to the plaintiff that the tendering procedure would be conducted in accordance with the principles of the Code ... by entering into a process of negotiation by which tenderers were invited to reduce their tenders and awarding the contract to the second lowest tenderer at his reduced price the defendants were in breach of contract.'

The measure of damages was held to be the cost of tendering, plus loss of profit, subject to a discount of 20 per cent for mitigation of the loss through availability for other work.

2.3 TENDER PROCEDURE AND CRITERIA: PRINCIPLES

As the Court of Appeal made clear in *Blackpool and Fylde Aero Club v Blackpool BC*, owners have traditionally had very wide discretion as to how they set up, and how they operate, the tendering procedure. To some extent, owners still have flexibility in these respects. However, several major caveats to this general statement must be entered to give an accurate account of the modern position.

First, a potential tenderer must not be invalidly excluded from the tender process. In *Ballast Nedam Group NV v Belgium*, it was held that a company could not be excluded from consideration for public works contracts on the ground that it would not do all the work itself. *Aquatron Marine v Strathclyde Fire Board* is another recent example of exclusion from the tender process on invalid grounds.

Second, even in the private sector, the owner is bound to follow the procedure adopted and set out in the invitation to tender. In the recent case of *J&A Developments Ltd v Edina Manufacturing Ltd*, the court took note of the owner's inclusion in the conditions of tender of the Code of Procedure for Single Stage Selective Tendering. The Code condemned as a 'deplorable practice' any attempt to seek to reduce a tender submitted in free competition.

Third, in the public sector, there are greater constraints on the owner's freedom regarding tender procedure and evaluation criteria. There is not complete freedom even where the statutory regime of procurement regulation does not apply: *Gerald Martin Scott v Belfast Education & Library Board*, where it was stated that procedures specified (in the tender documents) must be followed and assessment made according to the stated criteria. It is not only the owner who is bound by the procedure specified: in *The Queen in Right of Ontario v Ron Engineering and Construction Eastern*, the successful tenderer was bound by a provision of the tender conditions by which it would forfeit its tender deposit in the event of failing to proceed to execute a contract after acceptance.

A particularly important procedural principle is the avoidance of favourable or unequal treatment, such as communication or other engagement with one tenderer rather than all. In the New Zealand case of *Pratt Contractors v Palmerston North District Council*, one tenderer had been allowed to submit an alternative tender as well as the principal tender, and offered to meet the Council's representatives to discuss the savings to be achieved. This kind of unofficial and selective dealing is sometimes known as 'flirting' and was one of the practices condemned by the court in *Harmon CFEM v The Corporate Officer of the House of Commons*, where the client had engaged in post-tender negotiations with the successful tenderer.

It should be noted that, while scrutiny in the tendering process is most often directed at the conduct of the awarding authority, contractors have duties too. At the time of writing, a number of contractors were under investigation for collusion in so-called price-fixing. *Makers UK Ltd v Office of Fair Trading* offers further explanation of the practice of 'cover bidding' or 'cover pricing', by which contractors may seek to distort the tender process by giving a misleading impression of competition. Such conduct may constitute a breach of the *Competition Act 1998* and attract penal sanctions.

The tender evaluation stage is also of critical importance and the subject of a number of successful reported challenges in public sector cases. It has already been noted from the *Scott v Belfast Education & Library Board* case that assessment of the tenders must be made according to 'the stated criteria', i.e.

those in the documentation forming part of the invitation to tender. In *Harmon CFEM v The Corporate Officer of the House of Commons*, the owner had used the expression in its tender documentation 'overall value for money' and 'most economically advantageous'. Under the then *Public Works Contracts Regulations* 1991 (see now *Public Contracts Regulations* 2006), use of this expression without further explanation would not only not preserve the owner's discretion as to criteria for award, but would oblige the owner to award the contract on price alone. See also *Lianakis v Dimas Alexandroupolis* and *Lettings v London Borough of Newham* on use of sub-criteria without full transparency.

In assessing the tenders and applying the 'stated criteria', attention is concentrated on the owner's consultants or employees charged with tender evaluation. In *Pratt Contractors Ltd v Transit New Zealand*, the Privy Council set out what could legitimately be expected of the Tender Evaluation Team by tenderers. The evaluation would have to treat all tenders equally and would have to communicate the views honestly held by Team members. They could not shut their ears to information which might change their views and could not award different marks where tenderers scored the same according to particular criteria; but they would be under no obligation to give the same mark where attributes were different.

See *Lettings International v London Borough of Newham* on scoring of bids which fully meet a stated criterion at less than full marks; this is another *Public Contracts Regulations* 2006 case.

The emphasis on evaluation means that the onus is placed on the owner to select carefully those undertaking the evaluation.

In *Pratt Contractors v Transit New Zealand*, the Privy Council stated that a person who had previous experience of a particular tenderer and who held views on that tenderer, good or bad, was not disqualified from acting in the tender evaluation process. Nor was it necessary that they should be prepared to grant a hearing or discuss a tender with the tenderer.

This endorses the desirability of experience on the part of those conducting the tender evaluation. This theme was taken up in the recent Scottish case of *Aquatron Marine v Strathclyde Fire Board*, where the staff engaged in the tender evaluations had insufficient understanding of the requirements of the *Public Services Contracts Regulations* 1993 then in force and excluded a tenderer from further consideration on the basis of a criterion where no minimum level of achievement was specified.

Makers UK Ltd v Office of Fair Trading (2007)

The Competition Appeal Tribunal dismissed an appeal by roofing contractors Makers against the Office of Fair Trading's decision to impose a penalty upon contractors who had breached section 2(1) of the *Competition Act* 1998, which prohibits agreements having as their object or effect the prevention, restriction or distortion of competition within the UK. The breach in question consisted of participation with other contractors in 'cover bidding' or 'cover pricing', described by the Tribunal as occurring when:

> '... a contractor that is not intending to win the contract submits a price for it after communicating with the designated winner. The price is decided upon in conjunction with another contractor that wishes to win the contract. Cover pricing gives the impression of competitive bidding but, in reality, contractors agree to submit token bids that are higher than the bid of the contractor that is seeking the cover.'

The Tribunal was satisfied that there was sufficient evidence of a 'concerted practice' to comprise the offence; it is not necessary to prove the existence of an agreement in the sense of a contract to collude. Accordingly, the contractor's appeals against the finding of a breach and against the penalty were dismissed.

Aquatron Marine v Strathclyde Fire Board (2007)

The pursuers (claimants), who were unsuccessful tenderers for a breathing apparatus contract, alleged breach of a duty by the tendering authority (the fire service) to treat all tenders equally and fairly throughout the tender process and breach of the *Public Services Contracts Regulations* 1993 then in force. The court found a number of significant errors in the tender process, which had led to the pursuers being excluded from further consideration. In general terms, the staff involved in preparation of the evaluation of the tenders

'... did not possess the requisite expertise to process the tenders from a technical viewpoint, did not have sufficient experience to carry out the task of evaluation and did not have an adequate understanding of what was required of the defenders [the Board] in terms of the Regulations.'

Specifically, the clause which called for copies of evidence of quality standards achieved by the tenderer's workforce did not set out any minimum requirement in this respect for progress to the next stage. The limitations or failure of the pursuers in providing such evidence could not therefore be validly used to exclude any tenderer. The tenderers had not been asked to provide curriculum vitae for their staff and so could not be penalised for failing to do so. The pursuers' covering letter explaining which staff would work on the contract was not included in consideration of their submission, which constituted inequality of treatment as between tenderers by the awarding authority. The tendering authority formed the impression of inadequate staffing on incorrect information and proceeded to exclude the pursuers on that basis.

The correct outcome, therefore, should have been that both the successful tender and the pursuers' tender should have proceeded to formal evaluation, where they would have stood 'at least an even chance' of success. Since the criticisms made of the pursuers' tender were not easily referable to the original criteria advertised in the Official Journal, only 'price' remained, and the pursuers' tender was lower than that accepted. The tendering authority had failed to observe the 'principle of equal treatment of tenderers', even though the court observed that this was not explicitly stated in the 1993 Regulations. Damages were assessed on the basis of half of the contract value, plus interest.

2.4 TENDER PROCEDURE AND CRITERIA: THE EU PROCUREMENT REGIME

As indicated above, many contracts in the public and utilities sectors are governed by the EU procurement regulatory regime.

This affects tender procedures, as in the *Harmon* and *Aquatron* cases. It also affects the substance of the criteria which can be validly utilised by the awarding authority. The starting-point is that unrestricted freedom of choice, on the part of the awarding authority, is incompatible with the EC Directives on public procurement. The European Court of Justice stated this clearly in *SIAC v Mayo County Council*. The fundamental principles of transparency and equality of treatment of tenderers and potential tenderers are of paramount importance.

While it is only possible to include a selection of leading examples of decisions on whether tendering criteria are valid, these principles underlie almost all of them. The courts, and especially the European Court of Justice (ECJ), have been vigilant in trying to ensure that tender criteria do not favour tenderers from one nationality against others in an attempt to secure advantages for the domestic industry of the awarding authority. Thus in *Commission of the European Communities v Kingdom of Demark* (the 'Storebaelt Bridge' case), the so-called 'Danish content' clause was a breach of the Public Works Directive 93/37/EEC then in force; in *Harmon CFEM Facades (UK) Ltd v The Corporate Officer of the House of Commons*, the covert 'Buy British' policy was an unlawful criterion which had disadvantaged a partly French-owned tenderer; while in *Gebroeders Beentjes BV v State of the Netherlands* the ECJ held that the desirability of employing long-term unemployed in the project was only allowable as a criterion if specified in the tender notice, and above all if it did not have a discriminatory effect against tenderers from other Member States.

Many of the cases on criteria are concerned with the overall criterion of 'most economically advantageous'. A variant such as 'most acceptable tender' in *Gebroeders Beentjes BV v State of the Netherlands* would only be allowable as indicating the awarding authority's discretion to determine the most economically advantageous tender on the basis of objective criteria, as opposed to purely arbitrary choice.

A little flexibility was recognised in *SIAC v Mayo County Council* to the extent that 'most economically advantageous' could be interpreted to allow selection of the tender which, in the objective opinion of an expert, would be likely to lead to the lowest ultimate cost, despite not being the lowest bid.

Some flexibility is also evident in other judicial interpretations of allowable criteria. Environmental issues were held in *Concordia Bus Finland Oy AB v Helsingin Kaupunki* to be a valid aspect of 'economically advantageous' factors provided, crucially, they are expressly referred to in the tender documents and are non-discriminatory (this has been incorporated into EC Directive 2004/17/EC since the *Concordia* case). Health and safety were held in *General Building & Maintenance plc v Greenwich Borough Council* to be a valid aspect of the 'technical capacity' criterion under the then *Public Works Contracts Regulations* 1991.

To be transparent and non-discriminatory, criteria for award of contracts must be expressly stated in the tender documents and applied in the evaluation and award processes. The *Lettings International v London Borough of Newham* case recently highlighted the difficulty of making sub-criteria properly transparent.

In *Commission of the European Communities v Belgium*, the awarding authority had awarded the contract on the basis of figures not compliant with the criteria stated prescriptively in the contract documents. Also, recently, in *Lianakis v Dimas Alexandroupolis*, the ECJ, applying *Commission of the European Communities v Belgium*, condemned the practice by a Greek municipal authority of publishing sub-criteria and further guidance on weightings after it had embarked on the initial evaluation process. As in the *Concordia Bus Finland* case, also cited by the ECJ, potential tenderers would have to be in a position to ascertain the existence and scope of all the criteria.

Gebroeders Beentjes BV v State of the Netherlands (1988)

Beentjes was the lowest tenderer for a land consolidation contract let by a Dutch government body but was unsuccessful in its bid. Its challenge to the award was referred to the ECJ. The ECJ held that the criterion of 'most acceptable tender' was permissible, provided it reflected the awarding authority's discretion to determine the most economically advantageous tender on the basis of objective criteria, and not purely arbitrary choice. It was also legitimate for specific experience of the work to be made a criterion for assessing technical ability and knowledge under the Public

Works Contracts Directive then in force (see now Directive 2004/18/EC on the coordination of procedures for the award of public works contracts, public supply contracts and public services contracts; and see the *Public Contracts Regulations* 2006 in the UK). The tender notice had referred to the desirability of employing long-term unemployed persons on the project; this was allowable provided it did not have the effect of discrimination against tenderers from other Member States and provided it was specifically mentioned in the notice.

Commission of the European Communities v Kingdom of Denmark (1993)

The Commission successfully sought a declaration from the ECJ that the Danish government was in breach of its obligations under the then Public Works Contracts Directive (and under the EEC Treaty itself) in the tender procedure for the construction of a bridge over the western channel of the Storebaelt (the case is often referred to as the 'Storebaelt' or 'Storebaelt Bridge' case). The Danish government had included in the general tender conditions the so-called 'Danish content clause', by which tenders were invited on condition that the greatest possible use was made of Danish materials, goods, labour and equipment. The Danish government had committed a further breach in accepting a tender which was submitted as an alternative tender. While alternative tenders were allowable in principle, this one did not comply with the general tender conditions, so the negotiations with the consortium selected had been conducted on the basis of a non-compliant tender.

General Building and Maintenance plc v Greenwich Borough Council (1993)

The Council sought to invite tenders for a long-term £12 million repair and maintenance contract for its housing stock, which was a public works contract under the then *Public Works Contracts Regulations* 1991 (see now the *Public Contracts Regulations* 2006). The Council adopted the restricted procedure under the Regulations by which requests could be received for invitations to tender, excluding some potential tenderers on limited grounds. General Building and

Maintenance (GBM) was one of 104 applicants, but was not invited to tender, on the ground that its health and safety statement was inadequate. GBM sought an injunction restraining the award of the contract until GBM had been invited to tender, arguing that the Regulations did not permit health and safety to be taken into account. The court rejected GBM's application, holding that health and safety could be treated as part of 'technical capacity' within the Regulations. The Council had information on GBM's health and safety capacity and was not in breach of the Regulations in considering it. The court observed that:

> 'For many contractors, and certainly for building contractors such as the plaintiffs, ability competently to carry out the operations of their trade in these days includes ability to carry them out with proper regard for the health and safety of those whom they employ and members of the public whom they affect.'

Ballast Nedam Groep NV v Belgium (1994)

The ECJ, on a reference from the Belgian Raad van State, decided that the Belgian State could not exclude the Dutch Ballast Nedam Groep from registration as a contractor to be allowed to tender for public works projects on the ground that it was not a works contractor but a holding company. The Belgian government had taken the view that, as it did not execute works itself, the company could not demonstrate capacity or experience for the purposes of qualifying as a suitable tenderer. However, the court held that procedures for the award of public works contracts must permit, for the purposes of assessment for suitability for consideration as a tenderer, the inclusion of contractors as part of groups or consortia, provided they could demonstrate that they could actually call upon the resources in question necessary for carrying out the works.

Commission of the European Communities v Kingdom of Belgium (1995)

The ECJ held that a Belgian public transport authority had failed to satisfy the requirements of equal treatment and transparency in its tender procedure for a contract to supply 307 vehicles. The ECJ considered that the Utilities

Procurement Directive 90/531/EEC (in this case transport) then in force (see now Directive 2004/17/EC; and in the UK the *Utilities Contracts Regulations* 2006), would be breached by several features of the transport authority's conduct. Specifically, the authority had taken into account information submitted by the tenderer with its bid, had awarded the contract on the basis of figures not compliant with the prescriptive requirements of the contract documents and had taken into account cost-saving recommendations by the successful tenderer notice referred to in the contract documents or tender notice. These actions did not meet the Directive's fundamental requirements of equal treatment and transparency.

SIAC Construction v Mayo County Council (2001)

The Irish Supreme Court referred to the ECJ a dispute between SIAC Construction, a tenderer for a public works contract to construct a drainage system, and Mayo County Council, the awarding authority. The contract notice, as published in the Official Journal of the EC, provided that the contract would be awarded to the competent contractor submitting the tender 'adjudged to be the most advantageous to the Council in respect of cost and technical merit'. SIAC submitted the lowest of the 24 tenders received. The Council's consulting engineer found that the three lowest tenders were equal from the point of view of technical merit, but he criticised SIAC's pricing model, under which it had deducted a provisional sum for materials, to which tenderers were instructed to add a percentage for overheads and profit. He stated that SIAC's approach would reduce control by the engineer and hence a rival bid might give better value for money. The contract was awarded to the contractor submitting that rival bid.

The Irish High Court rejected SIAC's challenge on the ground that the Council had acted within its legitimate discretion and had not acted unreasonably. On appeal, the Irish Supreme Court referred to the ECJ the question whether an awarding authority, under the then Public Works Directive, having chosen to award a contract to the most economically advantageous tender, is allowed to award it to the tender, the ultimate cost of which is likely to be lowest, in the opinion of an expert.

Emphasising the principle of equality, specifically at the times when tenders are respectively formulated and assessed, the ECJ referred to *Commission v Belgium* and the *Beentjes* case; the latter to the effect that 'unrestricted freedom of choice as regards the awarding of the contract in question to a tenderer' would be incompatible with the Directive. The overall conclusion was that the Directive:

'... must be interpreted as permitting an adjudicating authority which has chosen to award a contract to the most economically advantageous tender to award that contract to the tenderer who has submitted the tender the ultimate cost of which, in the professional opinion of an expert, is likely to be the lowest, provided that the equal treatment of tenderers has been ensured, which presupposes that the transparency and objectivity of the procedure have been guaranteed and in particular that:

- this award criterion was clearly stated in the contract notice or contract documents; and

- the professional opinion is based in all essential points on objective factors regarded in good professional practice as relevant and appropriate to the assessment made.'

Concordia Bus Finland Oy AB v Helsingin Kaupunki (2001)

The municipal authority for the city of Helsinki published a notice, also contained in the Official Journal of the EU, calling for tenders for the operation of the city's urban bus network, in accordance with specified routes and timetables. The contract was to be awarded to the provider of the tender most economically advantageous overall to the city, assessed by reference to three categories of criteria: overall price of operation, quality of bus fleet and operator's quality and environment management. The tariff of points included bonuses for use of buses with low nitrogen oxide emissions and low noise levels (under 'quality of bus fleet'), for various certified quality criteria and for a certified environment protection programme (under 'operator's quality and environmental management').

Concordia (as it became) had submitted the lowest tender, but the contract was awarded to HKL, the city of Helsinki's own operator, which achieved a higher overall score due to bonus points for low emissions and noise levels. HKL and Concordia had identical scores on quality and environmental management. Concordia applied to the Finnish Competition Council to have the award set aside, arguing that the additional points for low emissions and noise levels were discriminatory, since only HKL's buses would be able to achieve them. The Finnish courts on appeal referred preliminary questions to the ECJ, to which the ECJ answered as follows:

> 'The position would be the same for these purposes whether treated as a contract under the public service contracts directive or the utilities (i.e. transport) directive.'

Where the decision to award the contract is stated to be upon the basis of the most economically advantageous tender, the contracting authority is entitled to take into account ecological/environmental considerations such as nitrogen oxide emissions and noise levels, provided these are linked to the subject matter of the contract, do not confer unrestricted freedom of choice on the authority, are expressly mentioned in the tender/contract documents and are compliant with fundamental principles of EC law, notably non-discrimination. *SIAC v Mayo County Council* was cited. The principle of equal treatment would not preclude the awarding authority from specifying and taking into account criteria connected with environmental protection solely because an undertaking connected with the awarding authority was especially well placed to meet them.

(Note that Article 26 of the Utilities Procurement Directive encapsulated part of the findings of the ECJ in the *Concordia* case, permitting awarding authorities to lay down technical specifications in tender documents which include environmental characteristics.)

Lettings International Ltd v London Borough of Newham (2007)

Lettings, a company specialising in property management, tendered for contracts with Newham to continue to manage part of its residential estate. Newham had advertised its intention to enter into two framework agreements, one for procurement, maintenance and management of housing and the other for maintenance and management of existing stock. After evaluation by Newham, Lettings was informed that its bid was unsuccessful. It sought an explanation, on the basis of which it commenced action, claiming that the council had not acted fairly and transparently in the tender process and had breached the *Public Contracts Regulations* 2006. Lettings obtained an injunction to prevent Newham entering into the framework agreements with other parties and this was upheld by the Court of Appeal, since damages would not be a wholly adequate remedy for the contractor.

Subsequently, the full trial was heard and the trial judge had to consider whether Newham had acted with sufficient transparency in disclosure and application of award criteria and whether there had been errors in marking the tenders. Referring to *Lianakis v Dimas Alexandroupolis* (and other EU case law), the judge held that Newham had failed adequately to disclose award criteria and weightings in advance for tenderers to consider. It had utilised sub-criteria which were not properly exposed and which were not, as Newham argued, merely scoring machinery. The judge found in favour of Lettings that 'proper disclosure by Newham could, and indeed, would have made a difference to the preparation of its bid'.

Newham had also failed in its duty of transparency in awarding only three marks out of five for those tenderers who fully met certain criteria and reserving the remaining two marks for those who exceeded the standard. This was not made clear to tenderers. The judge also found as a fact that there had been 'manifest errors' in Newham's marking, where Newham's officers simply could not explain why certain marks had been awarded. However, these were largely academic in view of the judge's overall conclusion, which was that:

> 'Newham acted unfairly without the requisite transparency and contrary to the regulations first by failing sufficiently to disclose contract award criteria and weightings in advance and second by failing to apply those criteria which were disclosed.'

His suggestion as to remedy, if Newham was unwilling to embark on a new tender exercise, was that Lettings should be added to its list of successful tenderers.

Emm G Lianakis AE v Dimas Alexandroupolis (2008)

The Municipal Council of Alexandroupolis in Greece published a call for tenders for a contract for professional services in connection with town planning for the municipality. The contract notice referred to the award criteria in order of priority as follows:

(i)   proven experience on projects during the last three years;

(ii)   manpower and equipment of the tenderer;

(iii) ability to complete on time in the context of other commitments/resources.

After 13 consultancies (including the challengers of the award) had responded to the call for tenders, the Municipal Council, having embarked on the evaluation process, issued further definition of the weighting of the criteria and added sub-criteria. Two of the unsuccessful tenderers took the view that the successful tenderer had only succeeded with the benefit of this further information and challenged the award of the contract. The Council of State of Greece referred the matter to the ECJ for a preliminary ruling.

The ECJ referred to Article 32 of Directive 92/50/EEC on the award of contracts for public services, which requires the contracting authority to ensure that there is no discrimination between potential tenderers. Article 32(1) of the Directive states that:

> 'The ability of service providers to perform services may be evaluated in particular with regard to their skills, efficiency, experience and reliability.'

Article 36(2) deals with the award criteria:

> 'Where the contract is to be awarded to the economically most advantageous tender, the contracting authority shall state in the contract documents or in the tender notice the award criteria which it intends to apply, where possible in descending order of importance.'

The ECJ held that Article 36(2), in ensuring equal treatment, requires transparency and that this would mean that potential tenderers would need to be aware of all the elements to be taken into account by the contracting authority in identifying the most economically advantageous offer (applying *Commission v Belgium*). Applying *Concordia Bus Finland*, it would follow that potential tenderers would have to be in a position to ascertain the existence and scope of all the criteria. A contracting authority, therefore, cannot apply weightings or refinements of criteria, such as sub-criteria, not brought to the attention of tenderers at the beginning:

> '... the Project Award Committee referred only to the award criteria themselves in the contract notice, and later, after the submission of tenders and the opening of applications expressing interest, stipulated both the weighting factors and the sub-criteria to be applied to those award criteria. Clearly that does not comply with the requirement laid down in Article 36(2) of Directive 92/50 to publicise such criteria, read in the light of the principle of equal treatment of economic operators and the obligation of transparency.'

The ECJ referred to *SIAC Construction v County Council of Mayo, Commission v Belgium, Concordia Bus Finland* and *Gebroeders Beentjes BV v State of Netherlands*.

2.5 CHALLENGES AND REMEDIES

Here again a distinction must be observed between private sector and public sector projects. If a contractor in a private sector project wishes to challenge the award of a contract to another tenderer, it would have to show that the tender contract has been breached. In the case of *J&A Developments v Edina Manufacturing*, the breach of tender contract by the owner was the failure to comply with the procedure which the owner had expressly adopted in the conditions of tender. If the case concerns a public sector project, the aggrieved tenderer could proceed either by showing breach of the tender contract, as in *Scott v Belfast Education and Library Board*, or breach of the public procurement regulations e.g. the *Public Contracts Regulations 2006*, as in *R v Portsmouth City Council ex p. Coles* (which was brought under the *Public Works Contracts Regulations 1991* then in force). In some cases, it would be possible to proceed in both, as in *Harmon CFEM (UK) Ltd v*

The Corporate Officer of the House of Commons (although obviously the tenderer could not recover twice for the same loss).

In October 2008, as this title was going to press, the *Construction Industry Law Letter* reported three decisions of the High Court in Northern Ireland on challenges by unsuccessful tenderers to awards of government contracts.

McLaughlin & Harvey Ltd v Department of Finance and Personnel (2008) and *Henry Bros (Magherafelt) Ltd v Department of Education for Northern Ireland* (2008) concerned applications for injunctions to prevent the award of contracts to the tenderer chosen by the awarding authority. In the *McLaughlin & Harvey* case, the contractor had tendered unsuccessfully for a place in a framework agreement for construction projects and alleged that the government had utilised a methodology for marking the tenders which had not been disclosed in advance. In the *Henry Bros* case, the contractor had failed to secure a place in a framework agreement for schools modernisation and alleged that the government had wrongly used the tenderers' fee percentages as the sole commercial criterion for award.

In the two reported decisions, both contractors failed to obtain interlocutory injunctions. In *McLaughlin & Harvey*, this was because damages would be an adequate remedy; and in *Henry Bros* because, on the balance of convenience, the delay and increased cost to the schools' modernisation was contrary to the public interest.

Public policy was also the determining factor in *McConnell Archive Storage Ltd v Belfast City Council* (2008), where a contractor unsuccessfully argued that the Council could not change its decision on discovering errors in its evaluation without application to the High Court under the *Public Contracts Regulations* 2006.

Since these decisions were made, Henry Bros succeeded in the trial of its action against the Department of Education. Coghlin J held that:

'... the original decision to rely upon the percentage fees and bands was based upon an incorrect factual assumption sufficient to amount to a manifest error.'

The award had thus been made unlawfully and the contractors' challenge was successful.

If an aggrieved tenderer intends to challenge an award, there are potentially two types of remedy available to be pursued: non-financial and financial.

2.5.1 Non-financial remedies

In December 2007, the EU introduced a new Public Procurement Remedies Directive (2007/66/EC). It must be implemented within Member States, including the UK, within 24 months. The purpose of the Remedies Directive is, as previously, to ensure that EU Member States provide contractors with an effective and rapid means of reviewing contract award procedures where the decisions made infringe either Community law or national regulations implementing it. Under the UK regime, which will be subject to some amendment (see below), the court has the power to order the setting aside of a decision or action taken in breach of an enforceable duty. While this is framed in negative terms, the effect can be positive in terms of outcome. In *Severn Trent plc v Dwr Cymru Cyfyngedig*, the application of the *Utilities Contracts Regulations* 1996 prevented the adoption of a non-compliant tender procedure by a water company following a takeover, but ultimately compelled the offering of the procurement of services for immediate competitive tender. In the *Severn Trent* case, the timing of the application for a remedy was one of the main issues. Timing has been a major difficulty in applying for non-financial remedies. The availability of injunctive/set aside remedies (the Directives refer to setting aside of decisions, rather than granting injunctions) is dependent upon the stage at which proceedings are issued. If a contract has already been awarded, there are rights of the successful tenderer, as well as the aggrieved party, to consider. In *Ealing Community Transport Ltd v Ealing LBC*, it was held that, since there was a gap between the Council's allegedly unlawful decision and the actual award of the contract, there would have been an opportunity to suspend the procedure, but once the contract was formed, the challenge would come too late and only damages, at most, would be available.

The position was even more complex in the celebrated ECJ case of *Alcatel Austria v Bundesministerium fur Wissenschaft und Verkehr* where the award, formation and execution of the contract were virtually simultaneous. The case led to the introduction, albeit as a matter of good practice rather than legal requirement, of the so-called 'standstill period', after the contract is awarded, to allow any aggrieved tenderers to bring a challenge.

The *Public Contracts Regulations* 2006 and *Utilities Contracts Regulations* 2006 have now introduced the standstill period (of at least ten days) into the regulatory regime. This is intended to deal with the *Alcatel* problem although, as in *Ealing*, it is still the position under English law that, once the contract is executed, any challenge intending to overthrow the actual decision comes too late; only damages are available to an aggrieved tenderer who can establish illegality in the award.

To obtain the non-financial remedies, which alone can actually influence the outcome of the tendering process, timing remains crucial. In any application for injunctive relief, the applicant must provide evidence of breach. The remedies regime will allow an application in anticipation of a breach of the procurement rules, as in *Severn Trent v Dwr Cymru Cyfyngedig* although, as with any anticipatory application, the evidential task for the applicant is greater than where the actual breach has already occurred. With this reservation, the aggrieved party would be better advised to err on the side of early action, since prior to an actual award, there may still be a chance to change the course of events. After the contract is entered into, the protection afforded to third parties by the procurement regime means that damages will be the only recourse realistically available.

2.5.2 Financial remedies

Damages can be obtained by unsuccessful tenderers in appropriate cases in both public and private sector contract cases. The EU Remedies Directives have long obliged Member States to provide, in their own regulations, for the award of financial compensation and most of the UK case law on damages is in public sector cases.

Harmon CFEM Facades (UK) Ltd v The Corporate Officer of the House of Commons is one of the most important decisions on damages, reviewing a number of different elements eligible for claim by the aggrieved contractor: tender costs could be recovered, as they would have been through winning the contract or, in the alternative, the value of the 'loss of a chance', if a re-tendering process was the more probable outcome. The case also established that a margin for risk and profit would be recoverable, as was, on the facts of the case, the 'intra-group margin', being the benefit obtainable to the tenderer of operating within its group structure for the purposes of calculating profitability. Aggravated or exemplary damages were not recoverable on the facts of the case and would only be so in exceptional cases where the effect of the illegality was 'oppressive' towards the tenderer. The related case of *Harmon CFEM Facades (UK) Ltd v The Corporate Officer of the House of Commons (No. 2)* contains guidance on the calculation of an interim payment of damages for tender costs and lost profit pending a full investigation of quantum.

In *Aquatron Marine v Strathclyde Fire Board*, damages were assessed on the basis of half the contract value plus interest, since the challengers would have stood at least an even chance of success if their tender had not been unlawfully excluded from evaluation.

In the private sector case of *J&A Developments Ltd v Edina Manufacturing*, damages included the cost of tendering, plus loss of profit, subject to a percentage of mitigation of loss for availability for other work.

R v Portsmouth City Council, ex p. Coles (1996)

The Council proposed to let three housing maintenance and improvement contracts out to tender, advertised in the Official Journal of the EC on the following basis:

> 'Criteria to be stated in the invitation to tender. Tenderers will be accepted on the basis of the best value for money. The Council do not bind themselves to accept the lowest or any tender.'

Tenders were received from the appellants, who were three firms of contractors, and also from the Council's own direct labour force (PCS). Council officers advised the Council's

Policy and Resources Committee that, while accepting the best value for money bid would save money on the Housing Revenue account, failing to award the contract to PCS would result in redundancies, involving the Council's General Fund in compensation payments. In the final decision, PCS got 40 per cent of the work under the maintenance contract, 60 per cent of the work under the improvement contract and 100 per cent of the work under a third contract. The three contractors challenged these awards as ultra vires. The court held that the award of work by the Council to its own direct labour force, PCS, could not constitute a public service contract under the then *Public Works Contracts Regulations* 1991. The Regulations applied only to one of the three contracts. However, where they did apply, the Council had breached them. In awarding contracts under the Regulations, the Council could only take account of the criteria specified in the contract notice or contract documents. In the absence of anything more specific, the criterion of lowest price should have been applied.

Severn Trent plc v Dwr Cymru Cyfyngedig (2001)

Severn Trent sought an injunction to prevent Dwr Cymru from entering into Operation and Maintenance (O&M) and Customer Services Agreements with a new service provider. Severn Trent had discovered that, following a proposed takeover, the services in question were to be put out to tender only over a seven-year period, instead of the 'immediate' competitive tender required by the *Utilities Contracts Regulations* 1996. It was argued that the application came too late and that damages would be an adequate remedy.

Langley J held that Severn Trent had applied at the right time under regulation 32(4)(a): 'promptly and in any event within 3 months from the date when grounds for the bringing of the proceedings first arose'. But this had been based on an 'apprehended' (i.e. future) breach, which was contemplated by regulation 32(4)(a). This could support a claim for an order as well as a breach which had already occurred. The parties to the takeover had proceeded as far as they had in the knowledge of the position under the Regulations and an injunction was proportionate and appropriate.

Ealing Community Transport Ltd v Ealing LBC (1999)

The company (ECT) had tendered for a contract to provide transport services for Ealing (the Council). On learning that the Council intended to award the contract to another supplier, ECT wrote to the Council alleging breaches of the *Public Services Contracts Regulations* 1993 then in force (see now the *Public Contracts Regulations* 2006) and obtained an interim injunction to halt the award of the contract. The Council then revealed that it had already entered into the contract and relied on the provisions of the Regulations relating to the protection of third parties in arguing that ECT could not obtain any remedy other than an award for damages. The Court of Appeal held that ECT could not challenge the validity of the contract once it had been awarded. Neither an injunction nor a judicial review could succeed unless the successful tenderer was deprived of its protection by some participation in unlawful activity or bad faith. Whereas ECT might have been able to convert their interim injunction setting aside the decision to award the contract, once it was entered into, that possibility was lost and only damages could be claimed.

Alcatel Austria v Bundesministerium fur Wissenschaft und Verkehr (1999)

The Austrian Bundesministerium (the Ministry) had conducted a tender exercise for a contract for the supply of an electronic motorway system. The contract was awarded to Kapsch, and signed on the same day. Alcatel and other unsuccessful tenderers sought to suspend performance of the contract. The Federal Procurement Office of Austria, the Bundesvergabeamt, rejected these attempts on the ground that the challenge came too late, after the contract was entered into. The question for the ECJ was whether a Member State was obliged to ensure that an aggrieved tenderer had a chance to have the decision annulled. The ECJ held that Member States were obliged to ensure that the contracting authority's decision is open to review. Where, as here, there was no gap between the decision to award and the actual formation of the contract, there was no such opportunity. It was in the aftermath of this decision that the 'standstill period' was introduced to permit challenge by aggrieved tenderers.

Harmon CFEM Facades (UK) Ltd v The Corporate Officer of the House of Commons (No. 2) (2000)

Harmon, having succeeded in its action against the Parliamentary client in respect of its unsuccessful tender (see *Harmon v The Corporate Officer of the House of Commons* at section 2.2 above), brought this case concerning the calculation of an interim payment of damages for tender costs and loss of profit pending the investigation of causation and quantum issues. The judge did not accept the client's argument that the amount should be reduced because Harmon's liquidation made it likely that any interim payment would be irrecoverable, concluding that Harmon probably would not have gone into liquidation had it been awarded the contract, as it should have been. It would get an interim award of one-third of its probable profit and would also be compensated for work lost subsequently as a result of its treatment. Account should also be taken of the effect of the appreciation of sterling against the franc. On tender costs, Harmon would get an interim payment of 95 per cent of the lowest figure accepted by the client's expert.

2.6 RECOVERY OF TENDER COSTS ON ABANDONMENT OF PROJECT

The previous sections of part 2 above have dealt with the question of an aggrieved unsuccessful tenderer's entitlement to a remedy where the contract is awarded unlawfully to another tenderer. This section concerns the possibility of recovery by a contractor of losses sustained as a result of the abandonment of a project by the owner.

The starting point must be that the client, the tender awarding body, whether private sector developer or public authority, is allowed to abandon a project at any stage, early or late. It cannot be the law under any legal system that a contractor must be allowed to build a project whether it is wanted or not – that is not the issue. The issue is whether the client's power, to proceed or abandon, is without cost to the client or whether it comes at a price.

The cost or price of abandonment may well be significant to the client itself. But in a number of cases considered below, the courts have had to deal with attempts to recover losses sustained by others, chiefly contractors, as a result of the abandonment.

The claimant need not be a contractor, of course. The case of *Stephen Donald Architects Ltd v King* concerns the failed attempt of an architect to recover payment, either on a contractual or quantum meruit basis, for professional services in preparatory work on a mixed residential/commercial project. In the absence of a contractual entitlement to the cost of the work done, the claimant was held to be unable to recover, since he had been participating with knowledge of the risk that the project would not progress.

In the *Stephen Donald* case, reference is made to *Regalian Properties plc v London Docklands Development Corp*. That case represents a significant obstacle to recovery of preparatory costs incurred by a contractor, not least because the sums claimed were not basic tender costs, but mainly professional fees for design work requested by the owners. However, crucially, there was express agreement that the parties' relationship was 'subject to contract' and that both parties were free to withdraw at any time. The expression of the parties' intention prevented the accrual of contractual or quasi-contractual obligations to meet any abortive tender or other costs.

In the *Regalian* case, the court was able, for the above reasons, to distinguish the position before them from a body of case law more sympathetic to recovery, at least within the limits of the factual situations in those cases.

Most of the cases draw a distinction between 'basic' tender costs and expenses going beyond these. In *William Lacey (Hounslow) Ltd v Davis*, the court regarded this as significant. In the initial tendering stage, contractors will incur costs at their own risk. The successful tenderer will recover its costs from remuneration under the contract. But if additional work is requested by the client, beyond that which is necessary to submit a tender, the cost could be claimed, not in contract, where none came into existence, but in quasi-contract (to use the language of the *William Lacey* case) or restitution, as it would be expressed more recently.

Marston Construction Co Ltd v Kigass, relying on *William Lacey (Hounslow) Ltd v Davis,* confirmed that the cost of additional preparatory works might be recovered by the contractor, based on a mixture of express and implied requests by the owner. Unusually, the judge felt that it might be impossible to distinguish in all cases between tender costs and additional works, raising the possibility of recovery of both, although most cases do make the distinction and limit recovery to the latter. The court also referred to *British Steel Corporation v Cleveland Bridge and Engineering Co Ltd,* where the court also laid emphasis on requests by the owner to the contractor to commence work in expectation of the eventuation of a formal contract. (See also section 3.1 on letters of intent.)

In the *British Steel Corporation* case, the court, citing *William Lacey (Hounslow) Ltd v Davis,* upheld the contractor's claim for quantum meruit, with an early reference to the principle of restitution.

Australian case law can be regarded as having gone somewhat further than any reported English case. *Sabemo Pty Ltd v North Sydney Municipal Mutual Council* is significant in applying *William Lacey (Hounslow) Ltd v Davis* to support the proposition that an obligation to pay for preparatory work done at the owner's request should be imposed on the owner. It also stands apart from any reported English case to date in emphasising the fact that the owner deliberately chose to abandon the project, which the judge saw as a factor in favour of granting a restitutionary remedy. This does not make it irrelevant in considering the position in English law: it applied *William Lacey* and was considered, although distinguished on the facts, in *Regalian Properties plc v London Docklands Development Corp.*

The role of intention in *Sabemo* was approved in *Brenner v First Artists Management Pty Ltd* and in other Australian cases. Although not a construction case, *Brenner* is valuable in summarising the position under *Sabemo* and applying *William Lacey (Hounslow) Ltd v Davis* and *British Steel Corporation v Cleveland Bridge and Engineering Co Ltd.*

Stephen Donald Architects Ltd v King (2003)

The claimant was a company, which was, in effect, an architect sole practitioner; the defendant was both a friend and potential developer. The defendant was considering converting a former public house, which he owned, into a photographic studio and flats. The claimant undertook some work, obtaining planning permission for the development. The claimant had proposed that he should obtain a larger sum by way of remuneration if he deferred his fees until the project was complete. When it became clear that the project as designed was not financially viable, the claimant sought payment for his work on the basis that there was a RIBA (Royal Institute of British Architects) agreement in place or, in the alternative, on a quantum meruit basis. He had received some £15,000 of the £125,000 he claimed.

The Technology and Construction Court rejected the argument that a contract had been agreed, although the RIBA Conditions had been discussed. The judge found that the architect 'undertook the preparation of the initial designs in connection with the necessary application for planning permission on a speculative basis'. The conclusion was that the parties had never entered into a legally binding agreement at all under which fees would be contractually payable. On the quantum meruit claim, the judge was referred to *British Steel v Cleveland Bridge and Engineering Co* and *Regalian Properties plc v London Docklands Development Corp*. He was prepared to accept that there may have been some benefit to the defendant in establishing the principle of the development through obtaining the planning permission, which might be of use in any future development. However, quantum meruit, being a restitutionary remedy, required unjust enrichment. Since the claimant had been closely involved in producing a design which could not be built profitably, knowing that this was the purpose of the project 'there is nothing unjust, as it seems to me, in Mr King retaining the modest element of benefit which he may have derived from the joint venture without paying compensation to Mr Donald additionally to the £15,000 which he has already been paid'.

The true position was that the claimant had assumed the risk

'... either that sufficient finance could not be arranged at all or that the terms upon which otherwise adequate funding was available were perceived by Mr King to be unsatisfactory. In other words, the claimant assumed the risk that at that stage Mr King might decide not to proceed. That is the risk which eventuated.'

The quantum meruit claim also failed.

Regalian Properties plc v London Docklands Development Corp (1995)

The plaintiff developer tendered £18.5 million to build on land owned by the defendant owners and the owners accepted 'subject to contract'. For two years, requests by the owners for further designs delayed conclusion of the contract, at the end of which a fall in the value of the site caused the project to be abandoned as uneconomic. The plaintiffs claimed some £3 million in professional fees in respect of the proposed development.

The court, rejecting the claim, held that the negotiations and the offer had been on the express basis that each party was free to withdraw at any time. The deliberate use of the words 'subject to contract' prevented any contractual (or quasi-contractual) obligation arising to meet any abortive tender and other costs. Distinguishing the 'pro-recovery' cases of *William Lacey (Hounslow) v Davis*, *Marston Construction v Kigass*, *British Steel v Cleveland Bridge* and *Sabemo v North Sydney Municipal Mutual Council*, Rattee J held that the law of restitution could not assist the plaintiffs here, as it had done in those decisions,

> '... where, however much the parties expect a contract between them to materialise, both enter negotiations expressly (whether by use of the words "subject to contract" or otherwise) on terms that each party is free to withdraw from the negotiations at any time. Each party to such negotiations must be taken to know (as in my judgement Regalian did in the present case) that pending the conclusion of a binding contract any cost incurred by him in preparation for the intended contract will be incurred at his own risk, in the sense that he will have no recompense for those costs if no contract results. ... by deliberate use of the words "subject to contract" with the admitted intention that they should have their usual effect, LDDC and Regalian each accepted that in the event of no contract being entered into any resultant loss should lie where it fell.'

William Lacey (Hounslow) Ltd v Davis (1957)

The plaintiff contractors submitted a tender for the reconstruction of a war-damaged property owned by the defendant. At the request of the defendant, the plaintiff provided more detailed calculations of certain elements of the property, including taking out of quantities. The defendant used the information in support of its claim for compensation from the War Damage Commission and then sold the site, so that no contract for the plaintiff firm (or any other tenderer) was concluded.

The plaintiff's claim for breach of contract was rejected by the court, as none had existed, but there was also a claim in quasi-contract (which would today be expressed in terms of restitution). The judge identified three stages in the award of a contract in this way: (i) the initial tendering phase, where tenderers incur cost entirely at their own risk, which can never be recovered if the project is aborted; (ii) a more advanced stage in the tendering process where a party has been identified and notified of its selection or otherwise encouraged to carry out further work on design or costings; and (iii) finally, if a contract does eventuate, the remuneration is governed by the contract and would cover all earlier tender costs. In this case, the additional work carried out by the contractors at the request of the owner had been 'clearly outside the type of work which any builder would be expected to do without charge when tendering for a building contract'. The consequence was that the court would imply a promise by the owner to pay the contractor for additional costings and calculations carried out once it had been identified as the likely winner of the contract. The judge found it

> '... difficult to think that any injustice will result if building owners, who obtain the benefit of all these services upon the understanding that a contract is to be given, should be required to make some payment for them, if they subsequently decide that the contract should be withheld.'

(See also section 3.3 on payment/quantum merit under letter of intent on this case.)

Marston Construction Co Ltd v Kigass Ltd (1989)

Owners Kigass informed contractors Marston that they would be awarded the contract for rebuilding a factory destroyed by fire for which Marston had tendered. The contract would be concluded once the insurance money had been received by Kigass. As HH Judge Bowsher put it, 'while all concerned firmly believed ... that a contract to rebuild would be entered into, it was also clear that in the unlikely eventuality which ultimately occurred, no contract would be made'.

Anticipating the arrival of the insurance money and the need for an early completion of the project, Kigass asked Marston to undertake certain preparatory works. Kigass admitted having known that they were leaving the contractors 'a fair amount of work' and 'that they would incur costs and that they would have to do preparatory work in the form of working drawings and an application for building regulation approval ... more detail had to be submitted to the local authority to satisfy the conditions attached to the planning permission'.

No contract was signed because the insurance money proved to be insufficient for the project. Marston successfully claimed remuneration for the works carried out, relying on *William Lacey (Hounslow) v Davis* and *British Steel v Cleveland Bridge*. The judge was clear that 'It was never alleged ... that the plaintiffs were told that any preparatory works undertaken before contract were to be at the plaintiff's financial risk'.

A notable feature of this case was that Judge Bowsher felt unable to distinguish between basic tender expenditure and the cost of the preparatory works:

> '... it is not possible without further evidence to draw a line at the date of submission of tender and say that everything that went before was part of the preparation of the tender and everything that followed was preparatory work.'

The basis for the contractor's ability to recover its costs was a mixture of express and implied requests for works which could not be characterised as simply part of the basic tendering process. The key was a benefit to the owner which 'may consist in a service which gives a realisable and not necessarily realised gain'. In the result,

'... there was an express request made by the defendants to the plaintiffs to carry out a small quantity of design work and ... an implied request to carry out preparatory works in general ... both the express and the implied requests gave rise to a right of payment of a reasonable sum.'

British Steel Corporation v Cleveland Bridge and Engineering Co Ltd (1984)

British Steel had undertaken some work for Cleveland Bridge in the expectation that a contract would eventuate. Despite 'protracted negotiations', no contract was agreed. British Steel made a quantum meruit claim for the value of the work done. Goff J, applying *William Lacey v Davis*, upheld the claim, with the following rationale:

'Both parties confidently expected a formal contract to eventuate. In these circumstances, to expedite performance under that anticipated contract, one requested the other to commence the contract work and the other complied with that request. If thereafter, as anticipated, a contract was entered into, the work done as requested will be treated as having been performed under that contract; if contrary to their expectation, no contract was entered into, then the performance of the work is not referable to any contract the terms of which can be ascertained and the law simply imposes an obligation on the party who made the request to pay a reasonable sum for such work as has been done pursuant to that request, such an obligation sounding in quasi contract or, as we now say, in restitution.'

(See also section 3.1 on letters of intent/award/appointment on this case.)

Sabemo Pty Ltd v North Sydney Municipal Mutual Council (1997)

Sabemo, having been identified as the successful tenderer for a development by the Council, were requested by the Council, over a period of more than two and a half years, to undertake considerable work in preparing and obtaining planning approvals. At the end of this process, the Council decided to drop the scheme. Sabemo claimed entitlement to payment for fees for the preparatory work done. Sheppard J in the Supreme Court of New South Wales applied *William Lacey v Davis*, observing that

'... it is now recognised that there are cases where an obligation to pay will be imposed (a promise to pay implied) notwithstanding that the parties to a transaction, actual or proposed, did not intend, expressly or impliedly, that such an obligation should arise. The obligation is imposed by the law in the light of all the circumstances of the case.'

The judge laid particular emphasis on one circumstance

'... which leads to the conclusion that the plaintiff is entitled to succeed. That circumstance is the fact that the defendant deliberately decided to drop the proposal. It may have had good reasons for doing so, but they had nothing to do with the plaintiff, which in good faith over a period exceeding three years, had worked assiduously towards the day when it would take a building lease of the land and erect thereon the civic centre which the defendant, during that long period, had so earnestly desired.'

The judge adduced the principle that:

'... where two parties proceed upon the joint assumption that a contract will be entered into between them, and one does work beneficial for the project and thus in the interests of the parties, which work he would not be expected, in other circumstances, to do gratuitously, he will be entitled to compensation or restitution, if the other party unilaterally decides to abandon the project, not for any reason associated with bona fide disagreement concerning the terms of the contract to be entered into, but for reasons which, however valid, pertain only to his own position and do not relate at all to that of the other party.'

Sheppard J specifically held as recoverable

'The direct cost to (Sabemo) of preparing the various plans and models and attending the various conferences which were held with the defendant and other authorities in connection with the planning and design of the whole project.'

Brenner v First Artists' Management Pty Ltd (1993)

Although not a construction case, this case contains a useful application by the eminent judge Byrne J in a decision in the Supreme Court of Victoria, applying *Sabemo v North Sydney* and English case law in:

> '... cases where a tenderer carries out estimating or other work in response to an invitation to tender for a contract. ... in general, the tenderer takes the risk that the tenderer will be unsuccessful and that, as a consequence, the work will be unrewarded.'

Crucially, though:

> 'It may be, however, that, even in such a case, an obligation to pay the tenderer will arise where the contract is not entered into by reason of a change of heart on the part of the proprietor: *Sabemo*'s case; or where the work done falls outside that normally expected of tenderers: *William Lacey*'s case; or where the work performed is of particular benefit to the proprietor: *British Steel Corp v Cleveland Bridge and Engineering Co Ltd* (1984).'

3
Award of contract

A letter of intent is typically issued by an intending purchaser of goods or services during the course of, or immediately upon the conclusion of, pre-contract negotiations. These letters tend to be issued to instruct the supplier or contractor to start work immediately, notwithstanding the absence of an executed contract. It may be that all contract details have been resolved and that work is to proceed whilst the documents for signature are prepared or other formalities completed. Equally, it is not unusual for parties to commence work where the contract terms are still under negotiation. Alternatively, it may be that the purchaser wishes to reserve goods so that the date for their delivery can be secured. This section is concerned with the difficulties arising from the use of letters of intent.

3.1 LETTERS OF INTENT/AWARD/APPOINTMENT

Traditionally, a letter of intent was regarded as of no contractual effect in most situations (see dicta in *Turriff Construction Ltd v Regalia Knitting Mills* and *Peter Lind & Co. v Mersey Docks & Harbour Board* below). However, case law has recognised a number of situations where the parties were to be treated as having respective rights and obligations following the issue of a letter of intent, although these cannot be reduced to a single legal proposition. In some cases, the issue is simple, in that it is not clear which of several tenders applied: *Peter Lind v Mersey Docks and Harbour Board*.

The leading case setting out the different bases of claim is *British Steel v Cleveland Bridge*. The possibility that work had been let subject to an 'if' contract was explored in *Monk Construction Ltd v Norwich Union*.

Whatever the basis of the letter of intent, disputes arise as to whether there was a binding agreement which incorporated the proposed terms of the eventual agreement, or as to the terms of the agreement (if any agreement was formed) under the letter of intent, however unintentioned. Of some interest in this regard are provisions designed to limit an employer's financial exposure and whether the contractor can recover amounts spent in excess of those limits. The decision in *AC Controls v BBC* provides a useful reminder of the need for care in instructions given where a letter of intent is revised or reissued or where the contractor is asked to carry out work that is inconsistent with the proposed financial limit. The outcome, as in *AC Controls*, may be that the employer unexpectedly does not have the benefit of the financial limit, despite intentions to the contrary.

Both *Mifflin Construction v Netto Food Stores* and *Smith & Gordon Ltd v John Lewis Building* are good examples of cases in which subcontracts were proffered but not finalised where it was found that the agreement was contained within the letter of intent. Procedural steps may also be significant, such as in *Fraser Williams (Southern) Ltd v Prudential Holborn Ltd*, which concerned a contract that was let 'subject to contract', or *Allridge (Builders) Ltd v Grandactual*, where the failure to implement procedures was decisive. Nor should the term 'letter of intent' be determinative as to the effect of the letter, as it may in fact result in a binding agreement: *Cubitt Building and Interiors Ltd v Richardson Roofing (Industrial) Ltd*; and see also *Harvey Shopfitters Ltd v ADI Ltd*. But where all contract terms were agreed, the mere fact that the contract has not been signed should not prevent reliance upon those terms: *Bryen & Langley Limited v Martin Boston*.

However, where a concluded agreement is signed, the failure to agree on ancillary matters will not be fatal: see *Mitsui Babcock v John Brown* and *Alstom v Jarvis* (see 5.2). Another possible outcome is that the entire agreement is found within the letter of intent: see *Hall & Tawse South Ltd v Ivory Gate Ltd* and *Stent Foundations Ltd v Carillion Construction (Contracts) Ltd*.

Particular difficulties arise where the contractor is asked to carry out work pursuant to a letter of intent subject to a financial limit or 'cap'. Considerable difficulties can arise where the cap is exceeded, as in *Eugena Ltd v Gelande Corporation Ltd* and *Mowlem plc (trading as Mowlem Marine) v Stena Line Ports Ltd*.

Some consideration has also been given to the nature and extent of losses arising, and extent of liability. See *CJ Sims v Shaftesbury* and *Emcor Drake & Scull Ltd v Sir Robert McAlpine Ltd.*

Throughout these cases, the courts may well find an agreement of some sort, through which a contractor is reimbursed costs incurred to date. Parties might well ask, 'Is this what I agreed?'. As Mr Justice Coulson noted in *Fitzpatrick v Tyco*:

> 'A method of contracting that sends out a letter of award first, with the proposed details of the contract to follow, may be common in the UK construction industry but it is a dangerous course to adopt, as the recent decision by Christopher Clarke J in *RTS Flexible Systems Ltd v Molkerei Alois Muller GMBH & Co* makes clear.'

See also *Cunningham v Collett E Farmer* under 1.4 for judicial guidance as to when different types of letter of intent might properly be used.

Turriff Construction Ltd v Regalia Knitting Mills Ltd (1971)

Turriff tendered for construction of a new factory and facilities for Regalia on a design and build basis. At the time, Regalia did not own the site and did not have finance in place, but were keen for all four phases of the development to be completed by mid-1972. This required a prompt start to be made in preparing drawings and preparing documents for planning consent. Regalia sent a letter of intent that read:

> '... it is the intention of Regalia to award a contract to Turriff to build a factory including production, stores, offices and canteen facilities ....

> All this to be subject to obtaining agreement on the land, and leases with Corby Development Corporation, full building and bye-law consent, and the site investigation being undertaken by Drilling and Prospecting International Ltd.

> Whole to be subject to agreement on an acceptable contract.'

Later, the entire project was cancelled. Turriff claimed the cost of some preparatory work in preparing drawings etc.

Per Judge Fay QC, a letter of intent is:

> '... no more than an expression in writing of a party's present intention to enter into a contract at a future date. Save in exceptional circumstances it can have no binding effect. ... A letter of intent would ordinarily have two characteristics, one, that it will express an intention to enter into a contract in future and two, it will itself create no liability in regard to that future contract.'

Judge Fay found, on the facts, that, pending award of the contract, Turriff had offered assistance in preparing drawings, and that offer had been accepted by award of the letter of intent, thereby forming what was termed 'an ancillary contract'.

Peter Lind & Co v Mersey Docks & Harbour Board (1972)

The claimant contractors submitted two tenders for construction of a new freight terminal. One tender was for a fixed price, the other was on a fluctuating price basis. The defendants advised that they intended to accept 'your tender' pending approval under the Harbour Acts and completion of necessary formalities. There was a steep rise in the cost of materials in the following months, after which the defendants confirmed acceptance of 'your tender' and arranged for preparation of contract documents on a fixed price basis. The plaintiffs refused to sign the agreement but continued with the work.

Cooke J held that the acceptance was imprecise in that it did not specify which tender had been accepted. The claimants were entitled to a declaration that there was no contract and they were entitled to a quantum meruit payment.

British Steel v Cleveland Bridge (1981), (1984)

British Steel supplied a quantity of cast steel nodes to Cleveland Bridge pursuant to a letter of intent which read:

> 'We are pleased to advise you that it is the intention of Cleveland Bridge & Engineering Co Ltd to enter into a sub-contract with your Company for the supply and delivery of the steel castings which form the roof nodes on this project. The price will be as quoted in your telex dated 9th February '79 ... .

The form of sub-contract to be entered into will be our standard form of sub-contract for use in conjunction with the ICE General Conditions of Contract, a copy of which is enclosed for your consideration ... and we request that you proceed immediately with the works pending the preparation and issuing to you of the official form of sub-contract.'

The parties negotiated terms of the subcontract but a formal contract was never agreed. British Steel supplied the steel nodes but delivery was delayed. At trial, British Steel's case was that no contract existed and that they were entitled to the price of the steel nodes as a quantum meruit. Cleveland Bridge claimed there was a concluded contract between the parties: they counterclaimed damages for British Steel's alleged breach of contract in delivering the steel nodes late and out of sequence.

Per Robert Goff J:

'There can be no hard and fast answer to the question whether a letter of intent will give rise to a binding agreement: everything must depend on the circumstances of the particular case. In most costs, where work is done pursuant to a request contained in a letter of intent, it will not matter whether a contract did or did not come into existence, because, if the party who has acted on the request is simply claiming payment, his claim will usually be based on a quantum meruit ....'

On the facts, it was held that the parties had ultimately been unable to reach final agreement on the price or other essential terms, the contract was not entered into and the work performed in anticipation of it was not referable to any contractual terms as to payment or performance. The defendant was obliged to pay a reasonable sum for work done pursuant to their request. Robert Goff J held:

'As a matter of analysis the contract (if any) which may come into existence following a letter of intent may take one of two forms: either there may be an ordinary executory contract, under which each party assumes reciprocal obligations to the other; or there may be what is sometimes called an "if" contract, ie a contract under which A requests B to carry out a certain performance and promises B that, if he does so, he will receive a certain performance in return, usually remuneration for his performance. The latter transaction is really no more than a standing offer which, if acted on before it lapses or is lawfully withdrawn, will result in a binding contract.'

He held that there was no binding executory contract, since the defendants' letter of intent asked the plaintiffs to proceed immediately with the work pending the preparation and issuing of a form of subcontract, being a subcontract which was plainly in a state of negotiation, not least on the issues of price, delivery dates, and the applicable terms and conditions. Since the parties were still in a state of negotiation, it was impossible to say what the material terms of the contract would be, and by starting work the plaintiffs did not bind themselves to complete the work. He held that there was no 'if' contract when, in a case such as the present one, the parties were still in the state of negotiation; it was impossible to predicate what liability (if any) would be assumed by the seller for, e.g., defective goods or late delivery if a formal contract should be entered into. Accordingly, there was simply an obligation on the part of Cleveland Bridge to pay a reasonable price for the work done and materials delivered. The counterclaim accordingly failed. Per Robert Goff J:

'... the true analysis of the situation is simply this. Both parties confidently expected a formal contract to eventuate. In these circumstances, to expedite performance under that anticipated contract, one requested the other to commence the contract work, and the other complied with that request. If thereafter – as anticipated – a contract was entered into, the work done as requested will be treated as having been performed under that contract; if, contrary to their expectation, no contract was entered into, and the performance of the work is not referable to any contract of which the terms can be ascertained, and the law simply imposes an obligation on the party who made the request to pay a reasonable sum for such work as has been done pursuant to that request, such an obligation sounding in quasi contract or, as we now say, in restitution.'

Monk Construction Ltd v Norwich Union Life Insurance Society (1992)

Monk was a trade contractor involved in construction of the substructure of a new shopping centre in Bristol for the defendant. The construction manager wrote a letter of intent to Monk in which they said:

> '... this letter is to be taken as authority for you to proceed with mobilisation and ordering of materials up to a maximum expenditure of £100,000. In the event that our client should not conclude a contract with you, your entitlement will be limited to the proven costs incurred by you in accordance with the authority given by this letter.'

Work commenced but no formal contract was concluded. Monk claimed its 'proven costs' which exceeded £4 million. On a trial of preliminary issues, His Honour Judge Fox Andrews QC held that no 'if' contract was concluded and that Monk was entitled to be paid on a quantum meruit basis. The defendants appealed. On appeal, Monk contended that no 'if' contract could be found, as it had not set out necessary terms and the parties were not ad idem as to the meaning of 'proven costs'.

In this case, both parties were bound by the contents of a letter of intent which had instructed work to a limit of £100,000. However, once Monk, with approval of Norwich Union, went beyond the authorised £100,000 limit, the Court of Appeal held that the terms of the letter of intent no longer applied and Monk were entitled to be paid a reasonable sum for works actually carried out, which in this case was a claim for £4 million.

Dismissing the appeal, it was found that there was no 'if' contract, since the letter of intent had only authorised expenditure to a limited amount, so that, if no contract was concluded, Monk could claim its proven costs. Per Neill LJ:

> '... there may be cases where a letter of intent provides a satisfactory basis for an "if" contract. It may sometimes be possible to imply terms which are missing from the letter of intent itself. But an "if" contract must contain the necessary terms. It must also be clear that the "if" contract is to apply to the contract work if no formal agreement is reached.'

Mifflin Construction Ltd v Netto Food Stores (1993)

Mifflin, the specialist structural steel-work contractors, had been issued with a letter of intent, the intention being that they would become a nominated subcontractor when the main contractor was nominated.

Despite meeting with the main contractor and agreeing details of the subcontract, including the programme, no subcontract was entered into. The judge found

> '... a breach by the plaintiffs of their obligation ... to conclude a sub-contract with (the main contractor). Clearly, the damages for that breach are the sums for which the defendants are liable to the plaintiffs under the letter of intent.'

Smith & Gordon Ltd v John Lewis Building (1993)

The letter of intent sent by John Lewis, as contractors, stated that the subcontract form NSC/1 would be sent by them for completion by the subcontractor. The subcontractor orally accepted the letter of intent. It was held that the failure of John Lewis to adopt the procedure which they had outlined, i.e. failure to send the subcontract, prevented them from relying on the arbitration clause contained within it.

Fraser Williams (Southern) Ltd v Prudential Holborn Ltd (1994)

Fraser offered to develop computer software on a time and material basis in an offer noted as being 'subject to contract'. Work was commenced following oral confirmation of the tender award. Fraser offered standard terms, which were not signed. Work was terminated after a short period. In a trial of preliminary issues, Fraser argued that the words 'subject to contract' did not prevent its offer being treated as such.

The Court of Appeal held, allowing the appeal relating to preliminary issues, that it was necessary to review the course of dealings, remembering that 'subject to contract' is conventionally used by a person to prevent being contractually bound, and accordingly the offer was not capable of being accepted. Per Kennedy LJ:

'Even if the proposal had not contained the words "subject to contract" so that it was an unqualified offer I doubt whether the letter of 10 March could be regarded as a firm order as it was conspicuously lacking in firmness.'

Allridge (Builders) Ltd v Grandactual (1995)

The dispute arose from conversion works in London where the employer had engaged a number of contractors who were all to carry out work on the site at the same time. The claimant, one of the contractors, knew that there would be other contractors on the site. Issues arose as to the terms on which the claimant had been engaged.

In a trial on preliminary issues, the court found as a fact that work had been let by a letter of intent and that reference had been made to the *JCT Intermediate Form of Contract (1984)*. No commencement or completion date had been identified. It was noted that the parties had agreed that the claimant would be 'paid weekly' what was properly due in respect of each invoice within a reasonable time. That was inconsistent with provisions under the JCT form. The failure to implement procedures under that form indicated that the acceptance of a letter of intent did not constitute a contract incorporating that form.

Following *Leach v Merton* (see 4.3 below), the court found that there was an implied term that the defendant would cooperate with the claimant so as to enable the claimant to carry out works in a regular and orderly manner and would not hinder or prevent the claimant from doing so.

Mitsui Babcock Energy Ltd v John Brown Engineering Ltd (1996)

The parties had signed a contract for the design, manufacture and installation of two heat recovery system generators for a power station but, at that stage, had not reached agreement on the performance tests to be carried out on the installed generators or the consequences of failure of those tests. The letter of intent stated that:

'... principal terms have been agreed through various correspondence and the detailed conditions to be the subject of early mutual agreement in keeping with the conditions of contract MF/1 1988 edition and the proposed amendments issued and discussed at our meeting.'

When terms were proposed, it was noted that conditions relating to performance tests were 'to be discussed and agreed'. Mitsui, the subcontract supplier and installer of steam generation equipment, later argued that there was no concluded binding contract, so that any agreement concluded was void for uncertainty and thus unworkable.

It was held that the document signed was a binding contract. The language and circumstances supported the objective inference that the parties intended to be bound by the term contained in the contractual document. The failure of the parties to agree on the performance tests did not render the contract unworkable or void for uncertainty. Per His Honour Judge Esyr Lewis QC:

'My review of the authorities leads me to the conclusion that there is no reason in principle why two parties should not enter into a binding agreement, even though they have agreed that some proposed terms should be the subject of further discussion and later agreement.'

In this case, the parties had agreed to a computer check of the design:

'Both parties signed the contract documents while they were awaiting the outcome of the GE computer check which they knew might lead to a solution. ... Neither party suggested that the signing of formal contract documents should be deferred until the result of the check was known.'

As the parties had operated the agreement on the footing that there was an agreement, evidence of that would have supported an argument that they were estopped from denying that there was a binding contract. His Honour Judge Esyr Lewis QC then went on to consider, obiter, the question of estoppel:

'Were it necessary, I would be prepared to find that it would not be fair and just in this case for BEL to resile from the agreement they purported to make with JBE in June 1993. I consider that both parties from that time, and indeed earlier, conducted themselves on the basis that they had a binding agreement. Ipso facto, I think they were representing to each other that that was the position. I think it would be unjust now for BEL to be able to walk away from the agreement in order to obtain payment for their work on a different basis from that agreed between the parties. The amount and terms of payment, which was the subject of agreement, are not matters which BEL say were uncertain. BEL received payments on the basis of the agreed terms and, in the months before they asserted that there was no binding contract, were asking for more money by reference to the terms of the June 1993 agreement. During that time the documents do not show them to be pressing JBE for agreement of cl 35 or tolerances and I consider it relevant that BEL's work was near its end when they alleged there was no contract.'

Hall & Tawse South Ltd v Ivory Gate Ltd (1999)

This case considered the situation where a contractor accepted a written offer by part performance.

The disputes arose out of refurbishment work to premises in Jermyn Street owned by Ivory Gate pursuant to a letter of intent dated 23 October 1995. Hall & Tawse was the contractor. A contract was created by the letter of intent, but it did not contain the arbitration clause that would have been in the subsequent written contract. The employer's letter of intent had required the contractor to 'commence the preparation necessary to achieve a full start on site on (start date)', the employer agreeing to compensate the contractor for 'all reasonable costs properly incurred ... as a result of acting upon this letter up to the date that you are notified that you will not be appointed'.

HHJ Thornton QC found that, by starting work, Hall & Tawse accepted the offer contained in the letter of intent, resulting in a provisional contract. The contract was a bilateral one which required Hall & Tawse to complete the works in a reasonable time for a reasonable sum. The written offer contained all the terms of the contract, but resort could be had to surrounding circumstances to construe the terms of the letter. Hence, as far as reasonably possible, valuations were to be carried out in accordance with the JCT provisions referred to in the letter of intent.

Stent Foundations Ltd v Carillion Construction (Contracts) Ltd (2000)

The terms of a letter of intent were agreed on 8 September 1998 as between Stent and Carillion. It was envisaged that the contracts would be signed under seal but several matters about the contract remained to be agreed. By January 1989, agreement had been reached on all the terms following the signing of a main contract between the defendant's next employer. The parties, however, never got round to issuing, let alone signing, the formal contract. Dyson J (as he then was) at first instance decided that all essential terms had been agreed and concluded that the execution of formal subcontract documentation was not a condition precedent to the existence of a binding contract.

Eugena Ltd v Gelande Corporation Ltd (2004)

Eugena tendered for works of renovation of a property. Eugena commenced work under the terms of a letter of intent which only authorised Eugena to carry out preliminary and design work and which imposed a cap of £50,000. Eugena left site at an early stage, but after carrying out works in addition to those contemplated in the letter of intent. The issue was whether Eugena was entitled to payment for those works and, if so, on what basis. This required the court to determine the meaning and effect of the letter of intent.

It was common ground between the parties, and the judge agreed, that the letter was accepted by Eugena by conduct and that the acceptance resulted in a contract. The issue was what the terms of the contract were.

Judge Hegarty QC rejected Eugena's argument that the contract was for the whole of the works and remarked that he found it difficult to see how this conclusion would assist the contractor in any event given the 'cap' set out in the letter . Construing the letter as a whole and in its commercial context, the judge concluded that the parties intended to contract only for a limited amount of work and that is what the letter meant. Also, the maximum that could be recovered was £50,000. However, the contract incorporated all the terms of the *JCT Minor Works Form of Contract*, save insofar as they were inconsistent with the terms of the letter – and the judge could not see that they were.

As far as the works not covered by the language of the letter were concerned, Eugena was not entitled to payment: there was no express or implied term in the letter providing for payment and there was no express or implied request for Eugena to carry out the work which would found a claim for a quantum meruit. Judge Hegarty QC noted:

> 'I think it is right to say that it was probably for the mutual benefit of both parties that Eugena stayed on site for a short time after the conclusion of the authorized works, though that inference becomes less apparent the longer the negotiations remained deadlocked and all sense of urgency departed. If, at the beginning of the project, in anticipation of a contract and in order to achieve an early start, Eugena had been asked to mobilise and put in hand start-up works, I think that a restitutionary claim of this kind might well have succeeded. But ... the principle cannot really apply where, as here, the parties have actually reached agreement for certain limited works and services in anticipation of a more extensive contract which may or may not come into being. In such circumstances they have expressly regulated the position pending negotiations and have imposed an express limit on the parties' rights and obligations. In the absence of a further interim contract, or at least a further request to remain on site, I do not consider that the law of restitution should provide any remedy beyond that which the parties have provided by their own contract.'

Mowlem plc (trading as Mowlem Marine) v Stena Line Ports Ltd (2004)

Where work was done under a letter of intent limiting Mowlem's entitlement to payment to a maximum of £10 million, the court refused to imply a term that the contractor would also be paid a reasonable amount for work carried out in excess of that figure. A term would only be implied as a matter of commercial necessity, and it would be contrary to commercial sense if Mowlem could avoid the upper limit on the right to payment by simply continuing with the work and exceeding it. Accordingly, the parties' relationship was governed by the letter of intent and the contractor's total entitlement to payment for works carried out under it was

£10 million. The owner was not prevented by estoppel or waiver from relying on the terms of the letter of intent.

Mowlem commenced work pursuant to a letter of intent which limited Mowlem's entitlement to payment to a maximum sum. As work progressed, the letter of intent was superseded by later letters with higher amounts, the last of which was subject to a limit of £10 million. Mowlem carried out work beyond that limit and for a longer period than anticipated. The Technology and Construction Court was asked to decide whether Mowlem was entitled to be paid a reasonable sum (in quantum meruit) for work it had undertaken despite the fact that the date up to which it was anticipated the works would proceed and the limit of expenditure imposed by a letter of intent issued by Stena had both been exceeded.

The court decided that the final letter of intent governed Mowlem's entitlement to payment. As a consequence, Mowlem were not entitled, on a quantum meruit basis, to recover payment of a reasonable sum for the work they had undertaken in excess of the limit. No term was to be implied into the letter that the contractor was to be paid a reasonable amount for work carried out and there was no estoppel or waiver preventing reliance on the terms of the letter.

His Honour Judge Richard Seymour QC recognised that a claim in restitution does not depend on an 'implied contract' and cannot be sustained if a contract already governs the situation.

Harvey Shopfitters Ltd v ADI Ltd (2003), (2004)

Harvey was asked to provide a tender to carry out works to ADI's property, which consisted of six flats, pursuant to the *JCT Intermediate Form of Building Contract* (IFC 98) conditions. In June 1998, Harvey offered to carry out the works for approximately £339,000. Thereafter, the architects wrote a 'letter of intent'. By the date of the letter, there was nothing left for the parties to discuss or reach agreement on. Nor, it was found, did they necessarily contemplate that a formal contract would be issued at a later date. The contract works were carried out and payments made as though the IFC 98 conditions applied. A dispute about the final account was referred to adjudication. Harvey then commenced proceedings, alleging for the first time that their claim was for a quantum meruit. ADI said the work was done pursuant to a lump sum contract. The crucial phrase in the letter was:

> 'If, for any unforeseen reason, the contract should fail to proceed and be formalised, then any reasonable expenditure incurred by you in connection with the above will be reimbursed on a *quantum meruit* basis.'

Harvey argued that this meant that the parties intended the contract to be 'formalised' by formal contract documents being signed, absent which Harvey was entitled to a quantum meruit.

The Court of Appeal rejected this argument. The court held that it was entitled to look behind the letter and to have regard to the surrounding circumstances. It had regard to the fact that the letter was the culmination of a procedure which had resulted in the agreement of everything necessary to be agreed. The Court of Appeal found that the words meant that the only circumstance in which Harvey would be entitled to a quantum meruit was if the contract did not proceed *and* was not finalised. The contract did proceed and so Harvey was not entitled to a quantum meruit.

The Court of Appeal maintained that there was nothing to prevent parties from making related agreements on different terms and that in this case a putative subjective intention to achieve symmetry did not support the existence of an objective mutual intention to enter into a Design Agreement on FIDIC (International Federation of Consulting Engineers) terms. Accordingly, the defendants ADI could not rely upon the cap on liability.

Bryen & Langley Limited v Martin Boston (2005)

Bryen & Langley were the successful tenderers in a project to carry out works for the owner, Boston. A letter was sent to the contractors, stating that the contract would be in the form of JCT 98, but some details of a bonus scheme and appendix details had yet to be settled. No such contract was ever signed by the owner. The contractors claimed sums due under an interim certificate and, when Boston failed to pay in full, referred their claim to adjudication.

HH Judge Seymour QC held that that the letter of intent had anticipated that a contract would be formed in due course on the terms of the JCT form, but the letter did not itself seek to incorporate that form. Thus, the adjudication provisions were not binding. It therefore followed that the adjudicator had no jurisdiction to determine the dispute.

The Court of Appeal heard the appeal by the claimant contractors against the dismissal of their application for summary judgment and their claim. The defendant submitted that the contract did not incorporate the JCT form and thus the adjudicator had no jurisdiction to adjudicate.

The claimant submitted that the mere fact that the parties envisaged formalising their agreement by way of a formal contract did not preclude the conclusion that they were intending an immediate contractual commitment to each other on the terms to be incorporated into the formal contract. The defendant submitted that, whilst the letter amounted to the making of a contractual offer, which was accepted by the claimant's conduct, it was not a contract in the JCT form, because the letter showed that the terms of the contract still remained to be agreed.

The appeal was allowed. The Court of Appeal held that all the terms of a building contract under the JCT form had been agreed and that, once the work had commenced, the contract had 'proceeded'. It disagreed with the judge's conclusion that the letter envisaged a formal contract being signed in the future which would incorporate the JCT form and therefore it was inconsistent to regard the contract created by the letter and its acceptance as incorporating that form. Per Rimer J:

> 'There remains the point that particularly impressed the judge, namely that the 12 June letter envisaged a formal contract being signed in the future, being a formal contract that would incorporate the JCT Form, and so it was inconsistent to regard the contract created by the letter and its acceptance as itself incorporating that Form. That is a view with which it is perhaps quite easy to have instinctive sympathy, but it is one with which, on the facts of the present case, I respectfully disagree. The mere fact that two parties propose that their agreement should be contained in a formal contract to be drawn and signed in the future

does not preclude the conclusion that they have already informally contractually committed themselves on exactly the same terms. Of course, if they negotiate on a "subject to contract" basis such a conclusion *will* be precluded. But otherwise it will not, or at least may not.'

(See also section 4.1 on express terms.)

CJ Sims v Shaftesbury (1991)

A letter of intent was sent asking Sims to commence work, adding:

'... in the unlikely event of the contract not proceeding, [the claimants] will be reimbursed their reasonable costs which have been and will be incurred and costs for which they are liable including those of their sub-contractors and suppliers, such costs to include loss of profit and contributions to overheads, all of which must be substantiated in full to the reasonable satisfaction of our quantity surveyor.'

Work commenced on site without a formalised agreement. Sims then claimed reasonable costs. The parties agreed that the letter of intent had resulted in an agreement between them (following *British Steel* and *Turriff* above). HH Judge Newey QC accepted that the letter of intent created a condition precedent so that the claimants were not entitled to claim before providing the substantiation required. The substantiation required extended to all costs claimed.

Emcor Drake & Scull Ltd v Sir Robert McAlpine Ltd (2005)

Where no subcontract that complied with negotiations between the parties had been proffered by the main contractor, the subcontractor was only bound to carry out work covered by short form orders issued by the main contractor under its express terms.

Cubitt Building and Interiors Ltd v Richardson Roofing (Industrial) Ltd (2008)

Cubitt engaged Richardson as roofing subcontractors at a building site at Hampton Wick Riverside in London. Cubitt sought declaratory relief that its terms and conditions were incorporated into the subcontract between the parties. A letter of intent was sent on 29 May 2003. The court found that Cubitt's letter of 29 May 2003 was in contractual terms an acceptance of the most recent offer. This was strongly suggested by the wording in the first paragraph:

> 'Please accept this letter as notification of our instructions to proceed with the manufacture, supply and installation … for the sum of £401,666.58, less the 2.5% Discount.'

Mr Justice Akenhead said:

> 'The fact that this letter was described in its covering letter as a "Letter of Intent" does not particularly add anything to its legal status. As has been accepted in numerous cases such as *British Steel Corporation v Cleveland Bridge & Engineering Co.* [1981] 24 BLR 94, letters of intent can evidence or create a contract where none exist or simply be an indication that a party intends in the future to enter into a contract with the other party. One must simply analyse in terms of offer and acceptance what if anything was agreed by or what agreement is evidenced by the letter of intent in question.
>
> The fact that, in the letter of intent of 29 May 2003, Cubitt indicated that it was the intention to enter into a "formal" subcontract in the future does not undermine the legal effect and purpose of the first paragraph in the letter which effectively is an acceptance of the most recently revised quotation.'

(See also section 1.3 on formation of contract.)

RTS Flexible Systems Ltd v Molkerei Alois Muller GmbH (2008)

The defendant dairy manufacturer wished to retain the claimant to supply services for automation of processes and equipment. After providing some quotations, the claimant was awarded the contact and a letter of intent was issued by the defendant, confirming its wish to proceed with the project 'as set out in the offer', subject to finalisation of price and completion date and stating that it would be using an amended version of the MF/1 form of contract, to be executed within four weeks. The claimant started work and negotiations proceeded, during which the letter of intent was extended for some three months. A final draft contract was produced but never signed. Disputes arose, leading the claimant to commence proceedings. The court held that the letter of intent had constituted a counter-offer. The final draft had never become binding, but after the eventual lapse of the letter of intent, the parties had reached full agreement on the obligations relating to the work.

3.2 POSITION OF CLIENT UNDER LETTER OF INTENT/AWARD/APPOINTMENT

A client may seek to rely upon terms, whether as part of a claim for breach against a contractor or to benefit from a contractual provision relating to, say, a preferred dispute resolution mechanism or insurance indemnity provisions. In those instances, the client will usually seek to rely on the contract, as occurred in *Mirant Asia-Pacific*. If no contract is found to be in place on the terms expected, the client will lose that benefit. This has already been seen in *British Steel v Cleveland Bridge* (above), where British Steel, on a finding that there was no contract, was unable to found its counterclaim for late delivery of steel nodes; and in *G Percy Trentham Ltd v Archital Luxfer Ltd*, where there was no agreement, for want of an intention to create legal relations.

G. Percy Trentham Ltd v Archital Luxfer Ltd (1992), (1993)

The case did not directly concern a letter of intent but rather concerned the question whether, following contract negotiations, there was ever an offer that was accepted so as to result in a contract.

Trentham were main contractors for the construction of industrial units; Archital were the aluminium window subcontractors. Archital submitted a number of quotations and there were then various offers and counter-offers. The subcontract agreements were never signed. The subcontract work was fully performed, but Trentham alleged breach of contract for alleged defects. Archital sought to deny that the dealings ever resulted in a subcontract.

It was held that the lack of formality in connection with a contract that has been both agreed and performed is irrelevant, unless it can be shown that, as a matter of fact, the parties did not intend to create legal relations other than by, say, the execution of a deed.

Steyn LJ held that, where a transaction has been fully performed, the argument that there was no evidence upon which the judge could find that a contact was proved is implausible. He added:

'In the negotiations and during the performance of [the work] all obstacles to the formation of the contract were removed. It is not a case where there was a continuing stipulation that a contract would only come into existence if a written agreement was concluded.'

Conclusion of the agreement impliedly covered pre-contract performance.

Tesco Stores Ltd v Costain Construction Ltd & Ors (2003)

Tesco and Costain signed a letter of intent, which invited Costain to start work and stated that the parties intended to enter into a formal contract for Costain to construct a store for Tesco on Tesco's standard terms. Under the standard terms, Costain would accept responsibility for the specialist design work of the architect that Tesco had engaged.

The construction of the store was completed but no further contract was ever entered into – neither party appeared to make a serious effort to finalise it. The store subsequently burnt down and Tesco claimed that this was partly due to defects in the architect's design, for which, under Tesco's standard terms, Costain was liable.

The High Court held that, although the parties had entered into a binding contract for Costain to commence construction, Tesco's standard terms did not form part of that agreement, despite the fact that the letter stated that the parties intended to enter into an agreement on those terms at a later date. Costain was, therefore, not responsible for the architect's work.

Mirant Asia-Pacific Construction v Ove Arup (2004)

This dispute relates to the design and construction of a coal fired power station at Sual in the Philippines. The claimants

(Mirant) engaged the defendants (Arup) to provide various engineering services for the project, including design and ground investigations. Unfortunately, two of the boiler foundations failed during construction and Mirant brought a claim against Arup for the losses which it suffered as a result in the sum of approximately US$63 million plus interest. One of the central issues was whether the relevant agreements incorporated the terms of the 1991 FIDIC Client/Consultant Model Services Agreement, which included a five-year limitation period and £4 million cap on liability. HHJ Toulmin CMG QC ordered that this point should be determined as a preliminary issue.

3.3 PAYMENT/QUANTUM MERUIT UNDER LETTER OF INTENT/APPOINTMENT/AWARD

Where there is an express contract to do work at an unquantified price, the measure is the reasonable remuneration of the contractor: *Serck Controls Ltd v Drake & Scull Engineering Ltd.* The courts have had to consider the basis upon which that reasonable amount might be calculated. Even in cases where there is a contract, the bases suggested have been wide ranging.

In the case where there was a contract, the assessment of a quantum meruit was usually based on actual cost, which would include on- and off-site overheads, provided that it was reasonable and was reasonably and not unnecessarily incurred, plus an appropriate addition for profit: *ERDC Group Limited v Brunel University.* The basis of assessment was also discussed in the Australian case of *ABB Engineering Construction Ltd v Abigroup Contractors Pty Ltd.* An extension of this is whether a cap or limit might be applied, or interest payable: see *Diamond Build Ltd v Clapham Park Homes* and *Claymore Services Ltd v Nautilus Properties Ltd.*

Valuation on the basis of market rates also has some support, but there is no need for the defendant to have received a benefit: *William Lacey (Hounslow) Ltd v Davis.* Consistent with this is the view that the unconcluded contract may be good evidence of the appropriate measure. In the measure of a fair remuneration and allowance for profit, consideration had to be given to the relationship of the parties and the competitive edge that the subcontractor had by the significant advantage of having already mobilized his equipment: *Costain Civil Engineering Ltd v Zanen Dredging & Contracting Co.*

Whatever the basis, the question also arises as to whether the proposed contract price should act as an upper limit to the amount recovered, a point considered in *Lachhani v Destination Canada (UK) Ltd.*

Haden Young Ltd v Laing O'Rourke Midlands Ltd provides another example of an instance where the parties did not sign a subcontract but where the subcontractor proceeded with the works and the contractor paid sums by reference to the terms of a draft subcontract.

Lachhani v Destination Canada (UK) Ltd (1997)

Mr Recorder Colin Reese QC considered that the contractor's offer in the unconcluded contract should act as an upper limit to the measure of the quantum meruit, even though that might lead the contractor to sustain a loss:

> 'A building contractor should not be better off as a result of the failure to conclude a contract than he would have been if his offer had been accepted, i.e., in practical terms, in a case such as this, the price which the building contractor thought he was to get for the works (because he thought his offer had been accepted) must be the upper limit of the remuneration to which he could reasonably claim to be entitled, even if at that level of pricing the building contractor would inevitably have ended up showing an overall loss.'

Mr Recorder Colin Reese QC recognised that a 'fair value' should include a reasonable or normal profit margin over and above the costs reasonably and necessarily incurred in properly carrying out the works and likely to have been incurred by a reasonably efficient contractor. He stated that there must be adjustment for inefficiency and defective work at completion:

> 'If the building contractor works inefficiently and/or if the building contractor leaves defective work then quite obviously the actual costs incurred by the building contractor must be appropriately adjusted and/or abated

to ensure that the owner will not be required to pay more than the goods and services provided are truly (objectively) worth.'

ERDC Group Ltd v Brunel University (2006)

Brunel issued five letters of intent and the authority under the last letter expired on 1 September 2002. At that date, 40 per cent by value of the work remained to be done. The majority of the works were finished by the end of November 2002.

On being sent contract documents for signature, ERDC stated in a letter of 3 December 2002 that it declined to sign, and claimed (for the first time) that it would only continue work on the basis that all work carried out by it would be valued on a quantum meruit basis, rather than in accordance with the Valuation Rules under the *JCT Standard Form of Contract*. Prior to December 2002, ERDC had submitted eight Applications for Payment based on the Contract Sum Analysis of the proposed conditions of contract and following the JCT Valuation Rules.

The defendant denied that this should be assessed on a cost-plus basis and argued that defective work should be taken into account. The court rejected the defendant's right to set-off sums owing, but accepted that the quantum meruit should reflect any sub-standard work and an allowance for delay. The basis for the quantum meruit would refer primarily to the rates and prices in the earlier work.

HH Humphrey LLoyd QC considered the valuation of work carried out after 1 September 2002, when the authority of the letters had expired. He held that there were no hard and fast rules for the assessment of a quantum meruit. All the factors had to be considered.

It was recognised that the circumstances in the instant case were unusual, in that there was a move from contractual to a non-contractual basis. He held that it was not right to switch from an assessment based on ERDC's rates to one based entirely on ERDC's costs. The move was not marked at the time and ERDC only made its position clear at a much later stage, by which time all the main elements of work were either substantially complete or heading for completion. A price or rate that was reasonable before 1 September did not become unreasonable after 1 September simply because the authority in the letter of appointment expired.

It was held that, whether the assessment is made by reference to cost or to rates and prices, the party paying for the benefit was not to be required to pay for delay or inefficiency. Accordingly, in arriving at the total payable by reference to rates and prices, it is necessary to look at what the contractor should have recovered by the use of those rates and prices. Brunel could not maintain a claim for breach of the contract, since the defects were in the work after the expiry of authority of the last letter of intent. There was no contract at that stage. There could therefore be no counterclaim in the classic sense.

His Honour then addressed the standard to be adopted in defining defective work. If the remedy being granted was restitutionary, the standard would be that attaching to the request. By complying with the request, there was accession to that standard. If the remedy was contractual, the standard would be that set by the agreement. He considered that, in practical terms, there was no material difference between the two approaches and none at all on the facts of the instant case, where the standards were the contractual standards that had applied prior to 1 September 2002 and which continued to be applied thereafter. In the case of additional work, the standard was set by the instruction or request. In the absence of a specification, the usual standards would apply – the design and work would have to be of a reasonably good quality and, in the case of work designed by ERDC, reasonably fit for its purpose.

HH Judge LLoyd then dealt with the measure of work that was defective, and dismissed a downward adjustment based on cost of rectification:

'In my judgment it would be strange if a defendant had to pay more than the true value of the benefit realised or realisable. ... In assessing what is an appropriate quantum meruit for the whole or any part of the work done after 1 September 2002, Brunel cannot in my view reduce what ERDC might otherwise have received by something like a set-off or cross-claim equal to the costs of putting the work right, except perhaps where as a result of what ERDC did or did not do, there is no benefit or value. Hence professional fees, e.g. on the cost of the work, could never be taken into account. Even so, in such circumstances, there can be no negative result. ERDC cannot have to pay Brunel or forego what it would otherwise have received. However since the benefit has to be assessed overall, if, for example, work which was otherwise up to standard cannot be used because other work was not done or was not up to standard then the value must reflect that result.'

HH Judge LLoyd dismissed the concept of mitigation as irrelevant to the valuation of a restitutionary claim:

'The net benefit to Brunel cannot be affected by whether ERDC was not or was given chance of putting the work right or an investigation as to whether it was willing to do so.'

HH Judge LLoyd held that for variations, the use of the rates in ERDC's March Tender Estimate breakdown was sensible. Such a contractual basis was in principle fair for the purposes of a quantum meruit, especially where ERDC's tender was not abnormally low but was close to others and the rates and prices shown in the March Tender Breakdown compared with the 2002 Spons Price Books and were objectively reasonable.

In assessing a quantum meruit by reference to rates and prices (whether contractual or conventional, such as those in Spons), it would ordinarily be right to see that something was included for the costs incurred should the execution of the works be prolonged beyond the period contemplated by the rates (taking into account the risks for which the rates must be taken to have covered, for otherwise there may be duplication) and a fair allowance for time-related costs would not otherwise be achieved. Assessment by reference to actual cost would not require such an exercise.

In a cost plus valuation, the overhead percentage to be used was that in the audited accounts for the year in which the work was carried out, which in this case was 12.66 per cent. For the valuation of variations, a figure of 20 per cent was to be used, comprising 10 per cent for overheads, 55 per cent for site preliminaries and 5 per cent for site design (which was not the actual figure but the figure that would have been adopted if a contract for the whole work had been executed).

As to profit, it was held that the actual return that the contractor would have made needed to be adopted as opposed to reference to the profit of others, in this case 0.7 per cent. This applied for valuing all work assessed on a quantum meruit basis. The figure was contemplated by ERDC for the project and near enough that used by it during the work. ERDC competed for the work and Brunel should not pay more than the amount which ERDC contemplated that it would receive. The figure appeared low but it was originally the margin for risk and profit. On a cost-plus basis, there was no risk; the amount was now only profit, so it was higher than ERDC might have received had there been a contract for the whole work.

William Lacey (Hounslow) Ltd v Davis (1957)

Barry J held that a quantum meruit claim could be made where the defendant had led the contractor to believe that the project would proceed, encouraging him to produce detailed estimates. The defendant had to pay, even though the contractor's work was ultimately of no benefit to him: the purpose was to assist the defendant in trying to negotiate a claim with the War Damage Commission.

(See also section 2.6 on recovery of tender costs on abandonment of project costs in this case.)

Serck Controls Ltd v Drake & Scull Engineering Ltd (2000)

The claimant carried out work on a control system pursuant to a letter of intent at a research facility for British Nuclear Fuels. The intention was that the defendant would be the mechanical and electrical subcontractor and the claimant their sub-subcontractor. At trial, it was accepted that there was no contract: the claimant was entitled to be paid a reasonable sum. The present proceedings were to quantify that sum, raising the question whether the amount due should be measured by the value of the work to the defendant, or what would be reasonable remuneration to Serck for doing it.

HH Judge Hicks QC:

'A quantum meruit claim may, however, arise in a wide variety of circumstances, across a spectrum which ranges at one end from an express contract to do work at an unquantified price, which expressly or by implication must then be a reasonable one, to work (at the other extreme) done by an uninvited intruder which nevertheless confers on the recipient a benefit which, for some reason, such as estoppel or acquiescence, it is unjust for him to retain without making restitution to the provider.'

HH Judge Hicks QC considered that the performance of the contractor, in terms of inefficiency and defects at completion, was a factor to be considered in the measure of quantum meruit:

'The site conditions and other circumstances in which the work was carried out, including the conduct of the other party, are relevant to the assessment of reasonable remuneration. The conduct of the party carrying out the work may be relevant. If the value is being assessed on a "costs plus" basis then deduction should be made for time spent in repairing or repeating defective work or for inefficient working. If the value is being assessed by reference to quantities, such matters are irrelevant to the basic valuation. A deduction should be made on either basis for defects remaining at completion because the work handed over at completion is thereby worth less.'

Hicks J considered that there was no duty to adhere to any particular contractual programme, for there was no contract. In the instant case, it was precisely the inability to agree upon a programme which was one of the reasons for failure to enter into a contract.

Nonetheless, Hicks J held that a firm working on a quantum meruit basis on a complex construction site could not wholly ignore the desirability of cooperation with others at work on the site. There was a duty at least not to interfere unreasonably with the carrying out of other works, and more positively an obligation to be aware of the progress of other trades and, so far as consistent with the firm's own legitimate commercial interests, to cooperate in efficient working practices. It was held that there was no breach by Serck of the qualified duty of cooperation to disentitle Serck from having its work valued on the basis of the circumstances in which they were carried out.

Claymore Services Ltd v Nautilus Properties Ltd (2007)

This case concerned interest payable under a contractual quantum meruit. Claymore carried out refurbishment work at the former Spanish Embassy in London pursuant to a letter of intent. The contract terms were not agreed and the contract was never signed. The final account issues were settled, leaving an issue as to the period and rate at which interest might be due.

Mr Justice Jackson characterised the claim as a restitutionary quantum meruit and held that interest should run only from the date when the sum due was ascertainable. As most of the information resided with the contractor, the interest should start to run when the contractor had furnished his final account and the building owner had a reasonable opportunity to review it. Where the claimant has delayed unreasonably in commencing proceedings, the court may exercise discretion either to disallow interest for a period, or to reduce the rate of interest.

So far as the rate that should be awarded was concerned, it was not appropriate to use the *Judgments Act* 1838 rate in a commercial case. That rate was for the benefit of unpaid judgment creditors, did not reflect the loss to the claimant from being kept out of its money, and could only be changed by statutory instrument. However, Claymore was a small business within the meaning of the *Late Payment of Commercial Debts (Interest) Act* 1998, and would not be able to borrow money at 1 per cent over base rate. The rate at which Claymore would be able to borrow money would be not less than 2 per cent over base rate, so that rate was awarded.

Diamond Build Ltd v Clapham Park Homes Ltd (2008)

A letter of intent was issued with an authorised upper limit or 'cap' for expenditure of £250,000. Work commenced but no contract was formalised. The court noted that this meant that formalisation of the contract would have to be achieved within a relatively short time period. One of the issues for the court was whether the cap was unfair.

Akenhead J was invited to, but did not, find that the cap produced an unfair position for Diamond Build. Explaining this, he said:

'(a)   It was always open to DB to commit itself to its subcontractors and suppliers in a similar way to that predicated by the Letter of Intent.

(b)   If the cap was being approached it would have been open to DB to approach CPH for an increase of the cap.

(c)   If the sole reason why the formal Contract was not being executed was the withholding of signing by CPH, the insistence by CPH that DB proceed beyond the cap would lead to at the very least an equitable claim for additional payment … .

(e)   The Letter of Intent, and the cap, relate to the work which was the subject matter of the tender. If additional or different work was ordered by or on behalf of CPH to be done by DB, that would attract payment in addition to and above the cap on a quantum meruit basis; that could be by way of a mini or implied contract or in restitution. Similarly, any breach of express or implied terms of the Letter of Intent agreement would attract damages which would not be caught by or subject to the cap.'

ABB Engineering Construction Pty Ltd v Abigroup Contractors Pty Ltd (2003)

The dispute arose from construction of a large arena used for sports events during the Sydney 2000 Olympic Games. Abigroup, a principal contractor, sought to engage ABB as subcontractor for the roof subcontract package. The package was awarded pursuant to a letter of intent. That letter dictated certain terms on which Abigroup required the work to be done and stated further that:

'Commencement by the subcontractor is deemed to be full acceptance of the terms of this subcontract agreement and confirms the existence of a subcontract between our two companies.'

ABB contested the terms, but began work. During the course of the works there was a dispute as to the required date for completion, following a request for accelerated completion. Abigroup responded that it considered ABB's advice to be a repudiation of ABB's obligations under the 'contract' and purported to accept ABB's repudiation. Consequently, ABB ceased carrying out work and commenced proceedings.

The Supreme Court Referee found in favour of ABB, awarding it $3,215,771.70 on its quantum meruit claim, plus interest and a further $1,855,971 in progress payments. ABB applied to the Supreme Court to have the report adopted. Abigroup asked for an order rejecting the Referee's award, based on nine alleged errors of law or fact.

Abigroup submitted that the Referee's assessment of quantum meruit was excessive and that the Referee should not have found that the only relevant consideration in valuing a quantum meruit claim was the reasonable cost incurred by ABB in performing the work.

Einstein J referred to other Australian decisions in which the Court of Appeal held that the contractor was entitled to recover on a quantum meruit the *reasonable cost* (as opposed to the *actual* cost) to the contractor of performing the works; and that the quantum meruit claim would not be limited in amount by the contract price following repudiation.

His Honour referred to a series of cases including *Sabemo Pty Ltd v North Sydney Municipal Mutual Council, Brenner v First Artists' Management Pty Ltd, William Lacey (Hounslow) Ltd v David* (see section 2 above). All are cases that concern the assessment of claims for work done during the tender phase, over and above that which is ordinarily done gratuitously in the hope of work. His Honour noted that, in the circumstances of the case before him, it was open to the Referee to find that the work carried out fell outside that normally expected of tenderers.

The assessment must have regard to what the recipient would have had to pay to obtain the services under a normal commercial arrangement. The cost incurred by the plaintiff in performing the services is not determinative of what is fair and reasonable, although it will be evidence.

Haden Young Ltd v Laing O'Rourke Midlands Ltd (2008)

LOR was the main contractor for construction of new facilities for Coventry City Football Club. HYL was the M&E subcontractor. No subcontract document was ever signed by LOR and HYL, and a dispute arose as to the existence of a contract between them. HYL contended that no subcontract came into existence and LOR disputed this.

This judgment was concerned with various issues relating to the existence of a contract and the nature of the legal obligations between HYL and LOR. Ramsey J said that he first considered the principles of law to be applied in cases where no contract has been signed and where negotiations have continued in correspondence and at meetings during the course of the project. In such cases, the courts have had to analyse what passes between the parties to see whether, objectively, they have come to an agreement on all essential terms.

After referring to *Pagnan* and *Percy Trentham*, Ramsay J concluded that the passage in *Keating on Building Contracts* (8th edition) at paragraph 2-017 properly reflected the law on those points.

3.4 EFFECT OF TERMINATION OF WORKING UNDER A LETTER OF INTENT/AWARD/APPOINTMENT

Standard form contracts contain detailed termination provisions under which either party, subject to the terms, might terminate. More importantly, those terms provide for the financial settlement arising from termination. Where work is commenced pursuant to a letter of intent, and before the main contract is formalised, and where work is terminated, it is usual that one party will seek to rely upon the terms of the contract to be formalised. Whether those terms are incorporated into the agreement formed under the letter of intent is often an issue, as arose particularly in *Jarvis v Galliard Homes*.

The case of *AC Controls Ltd v BBC* turned on termination under the terms of the letter of intent. A cap in a letter of intent was construed as a trigger point at which the BBC was entitled to terminate works. It did not do so, with the result that ACC was entitled to payment on a quantum meruit basis for all works not covered by the letter of intent.

Jarvis Interiors Ltd v Galliard Homes (2000)

Galliard was developing Old Sun Wharf, London into 36 flats and sought to engage Jarvis as contractor. There was included within the tender documents a provision that the contract was to be executed as a deed under seal. Galliard issued a letter of intent which provided:

> 'In the event that we do not enter into a formal contract with you through no fault of Jarvis Interiors, you will be reimbursed all fair and reasonable costs incurred and these will be assessed on a quantum meruit basis.'

Work started on site and continued without a formal agreement being concluded. Further discussions also took place. Midway through the project, Galliard's quantity surveyor sent to Jarvis articles of agreement, contract sum analysis, drawings and a specification for signature and proposed a supplementary agreement to accommodate, among other things, the guaranteed maximum price. In June 1996, Galliard purported to terminate the contract under clause 27.2.1.2 of the JCT Conditions. Jarvis said there was no contract and issued a writ for the work it had done on the alternative bases either that there was a contractual right to payment pursuant to the letter of intent or on a quantum meruit. Galliard applied for a stay under section 4 of the *Arbitration Act* 1980.

Galliard argued that a formal contract incorporating an arbitration clause came into existence when the requirement for a contract signed as a deed had been overtaken by the 'handshake agreement'. The Court of Appeal disagreed. Evans LJ noted:

> 'For the purposes of defending the quantum meruit claim, it was necessary for Galliard to show that the work for which Jarvis was claiming remuneration was done under the terms of a contract other than that which was contained in the Letter of Intent. ... The judge rightly rejected their submission that the Letter of Intent was a "formal" contract for carrying out the works. It clearly was not. It was expressly provisional, taking effect only until a

formal contract was entered into, and it may have had no more than, contingent status of an unilateral contract: "if you proceed with these works before a contract is entered into, then we will pay you a quantum meruit for them".'

The only remaining submission was that the contract came into effect when the parties shook hands on the agreement of the price. Evans LJ noted that when two experienced businesspeople shake hands on what they regard as a deal, he was, and thought the courts always are, loathe to hold that no legally binding contract came into existence. In this instance, it was found that no contract was formed.

Lindsay J (with whom Schiemann LJ and Evans LJ agreed), having noted the 'broad disposition to find a contract if one can' found that (a) the effect of the provisions in the tender documents was that there could be no contract unless and until there was a deed between the parties – the effect was akin to the phrase 'subject to contract'; and (b) nothing that occurred afterwards overtook that – this included the 'handshake agreement', which was itself subject to a formal contract being entered into.

AC Controls Ltd v British Broadcasting Corporation (2002), (2003)

The case concerned the installation of an integrated access control system to the BBC's 57 premises across the UK. On 4 June 1999, the BBC issued a 'letter of intent' to ACC. The letter of intent contained a number of detailed provisions. In particular, it stated:

'Subject to the terms of this letter, ACC is authorised to proceed with the works up to a total value of £250,000 or any other sum which may subsequently be notified to you in writing by the BBC.'

The cap was subsequently increased by another letter of intent issued on 7 July 1999. ACC carried out works to a total value of £2 million, and after the termination of the relationship between the parties sought payment of that sum.

In summary, ACC argued that the letter of intent constituted a contract requiring ACC to carry out and complete the entire project on the terms of the letter unless and until the letter was superseded by a formal contract.

The BBC argued that the letter was a true letter of intent; that it authorised but did not commit ACC to start work; that either side could terminate the relationship without notice; and that the financial cap of £1 million precluded ACC claiming more than that sum.

It was held that the effect of the letter of 7 July 1999 was to constitute a major and fundamental variation to the original letter of intent. It was in reality a second offer to enter into a second 'if' contract. The terms of this second offer were that ACC was to embark on the access control system project and start to carry out all the work involved that was defined in the specification and associated documents. It followed that ACC was being authorised to start to undertake all remaining access control work in accordance with the agreed programme. This created a difficulty, in that the letter of 7 July concluded with the sentence 'All other terms and condition of our letter of 4 June 1999 remained unaffected' but these terms and conditions were wholly unsuited to the installation and procurement programme work that was now being instructed. The contractual position as to payment was that a reasonable sum was due.

The BBC believed that the variously revised provisions, capping payment at £250,000, £500,000, £750,000 and £1 million, imposed a ceiling of recovery by ACC irrespective of the reasonable value of the work it had carried out. This could not be correct. ACC had agreed to carry on with the specified work at least until it was told to stop. It must be entitled to a reasonable payment for all the work which had been done on that basis. The effect of the cap was simply that the BBC was entitled to terminate once the existing cap had been exceeded but it was not entitled not to pay for work which had been properly done, since ACC had no right to terminate at will.

It was held that the spending cap was not intended to limit the amount that ACC could recover, but was intended to operate as a 'trigger', entitling the BBC to terminate the contract any time after the cap was reached. ACC was required to carry on working and was entitled to payment of a reasonable value for the work done.

HHJ Thornton QC summarised the relevant principles to be derived from the leading authorities on letters of intent (including *Turriff, British Steel, Pagnan,* and *Archital Luxfer*):

- A document called or treated by the parties as a letter of intent may, on analysis, give rise to a binding contract, if that is the effect of the language of the parties when objectively construed. That contract is one in which, pending the entering into of a formal contract governing the whole of the project, the parties have assumed reciprocal obligations towards each whose content is defined by the terms of the document.

- Alternatively the document may, on an objective construction of its terms, give rise to an 'if' contract whereby one party makes a standing offer to the other that if it carries out the defined performance of services that other party will be remunerated for that performance. However, no obligation to perform is created and the reciprocal obligation to remunerate is limited by the express and implied terms of the offer.

- It is possible for a contract to come into being without the conclusion of the formalities of the signing and execution of formal contract documents if a transaction is fully performed and all obstacles to the formation of a contract are removed in the negotiations and during the performance of the contract.

- In construing and giving effect to the language of a letter of intent, it is necessary to take into account the factual background out of which the letter of intent arose.

HHJ Thornton QC concluded that when the detailed provisions of the letter of intent were properly construed, the financial limit did not apply and ACC was entitled to claim the full value of the work it had carried out.

Diamond Build Ltd v Clapham Park Homes Ltd (2008)

The issues in this case revolved around whether the letter of intent had been superseded by a contract incorporating the *JCT Intermediate Form of Building Contract (2005 edition)*. The claimant sought a declaration that, by the time its relationship with the defendant was terminated, the letter of intent had been replaced by the standard form contract.

Akenhead J concluded that the letter of intent and its acceptance gave rise to a relatively simple form of contract. Whilst the first paragraph merely confirmed an intention to enter into a contract, the second paragraph effectively asked DB to proceed with the work. There was an undertaking in effect pending the execution of a formal contract to pay for DB's reasonable costs, albeit up to a specific sum. The fact that the undertakings given in the letter were to be 'wholly extinguished' upon the execution of the formal contract pointed very strongly to those undertakings having legal and enforceable effect until the execution of the formal contract. The fact that the specification referred to in the letter required a contract under seal demonstrates that the parties were operating with that in mind. The very fact that DB was asked to (and did) sign, in effect, by way of acceptance, the letter of intent, points clearly to the creation of a contract based on the terms of the letter of intent itself.

Although this was a simple contractual arrangement, it was found to have sufficient certainty: there was a commencement date, requirement to proceed regularly and diligently, a completion date, an overall contract sum and an undertaking to pay reasonable costs in the interim.

4
Contents of contract

Up to a point, it is impossible to generalise about the provisions of a contract, which can be as various as the project demands or as the parties wish. In any event, this book is concerned with procurement and the process of contracting, rather than trying to provide a commentary on terms of contracts. Nevertheless, there are legal constraints and considerations which mean that it would be quite wrong to speak of total freedom of contract. This section deals with those constraints and considerations as they have affected construction contracts, both standard form and bespoke, and which should therefore be in the minds of the parties and their advisers at the time of negotiation and conclusion of a construction contract. It is divided into (1) express terms and (2) implied terms.

4.1 EXPRESS TERMS

As a general principle, in English law, parties are free to agree whatever terms they choose. A party is free to make a bad bargain as well as a good one. If a party accepts a term which is very onerous, prima facie that party should be bound by it. However, there are certain qualifications to this general principle which should be considered at the stage of negotiation and formation of the contract. They are:

- the contra proferentem principle;
- invalidity of penalty clauses;
- contractual terms invalidated by statute.

4.1.1 The contra proferentem principle

The standard text book on construction contracts, *Keating on Construction Contracts* (8th edition, 2006, by Stephen Furst QC and Sir Vivian Ramsay), defines the principle as follows (p.61):

'... if there is an ambiguity in a document which all the other methods of construction have failed to resolve so that there are two alternative meanings to certain words, the court may construe the words against the party who put forward the document and give effect to the meaning more favourable to the other party.'

So the onus is on the party (and its advisers) preparing the document to ensure that there is no ambiguity of meaning. This is especially so where the provisions bear harshly upon the other party, since a court or other tribunal may be unwilling to see the party who prepared a one-sided contract obtain the benefit of its own unclear drafting. Thus in *Billyack v Leyland Construction*, the contractors, Leyland, could not prevent the plaintiff owners from recovering the cost of remedial works for defects through reliance on contractual provisions in Leyland's contract which they argued diluted their obligation to build in a workmanlike manner. The court found 'some degree of ambiguity', which was enough.

Similarly, in *Rosehaugh Stanhope (Broadgate Phase 6) plc and Rosehaugh Stanhope (Broadgate Phase 7) plc v Redpath Dorman Long Ltd*, the Court of Appeal rejected the owners' view of the effect of its own construction management contract, and, satisfied that there was ambiguity, adopted the interpretation less favourable to the party responsible for producing the document.

However, the contra proferentem principle will not apply to two important categories of contract, namely those which have been the subject of genuine negotiation between the parties (i.e. the terms, not merely the price) and also those standard forms which have been formulated by representatives from different sides of industry, such as the Joint Contracts Tribunal (JCT). This latter point was established in *Tersons Ltd v Stevenage Development Corporation*, where it was made clear that a contract prepared in this way is not to be treated as an 'imposed standard contract' so that there would be no presumption in favour of either party's position in the event of ambiguity.

When, in *Peak Construction (Liverpool) Ltd v McKinney Foundations Ltd*, the court referred to 'printed forms of contract' being construed 'strictly contra proferentem', it clearly meant printed forms produced by the client, as in that case, rather than industry standard forms, as in the *Tersons* case.

Most recently, in *Steria Ltd v Sigma Wireless Communications Ltd*, the court laid greater emphasis on identifying whether only one party benefited from the ambiguity than ascertaining who had put forward the particular provision.

Billyack v Leyland Construction Co Ltd (1968)

The defendant contractors, Leyland, undertook to provide a house for the plaintiff owners, utilising a form of contract produced by Leyland. After completion of construction, structural defects became apparent and the owners claimed the cost of remedial works. The contractors sought to rely upon the provision of the contract which said that the structural works were to be carried out to the satisfaction of the local authority and in accordance with its building regulations. Since that had been given by the authority on completion, the contractors argued that they had discharged their obligation.

However, Edmund Davies LJ (sitting in the High Court) rejected this argument:

> 'If there be any ambiguity in the building contract drawn up by the defendants in the present case, it must, of course, be interpreted *contra proferentem*. Putting the plaintiff's case at its lowest, I think the contract can be said to contain some degree of ambiguity if (as is urged by the defendants here) their primary express undertaking to build and complete in a workmanlike manner was intended by them to be limited and controlled by the words next following. Viewed in that light, the expression of satisfaction by the local authority does not, in my judgment, prevent the plaintiff from recovering.'

Rosehaugh Stanhope (Broadgate Phase 6) plc and Rosehaugh Stanhope (Broadgate Phase 7) plc v Redpath Dorman Long Ltd (1990)

The defendant structural steel contractors entered into trade contracts with the plaintiff owners of the Broadgate Development for the supply and erection of structural steel under a construction management arrangement. Clause 19 of the trade contract provided that the owners' construction manager could fix, by estimate, the amount to be paid by the trade contractor forthwith to the owners in respect of any breach, such estimate to be binding and conclusive until final ascertainment or agreement. At first instance, the owners obtained judgment for the amounts estimated as due by their construction manager. The Court of Appeal allowed the appeal by the trade contractor.

Bingham LJ rejected the owners' view of the effect of clause 19, adding in reference to the contra proferentem principle, 'I consider these provisions to be ambiguous and so adopt the construction less favourable to the plaintiffs whose document it is'. Nourse LJ was equally forthright:

> 'I absolutely decline, on the words of this contract, to impute to the parties an intention that the Construction Manager should have power to impose on the Trade Contractor a liability which is neither admitted nor proved to exist at the time, which may later be proved never to have existed at all, but which may in the meantime have brought him into bankruptcy ... .'

Peak Construction (Liverpool) Ltd v McKinney Foundations Ltd (1970)

In a dispute between main contractor and foundation piling subcontractor on a multi-storey flats project, the court had to consider whether the main contractor could reclaim liquidated damages it had paid to the client local authority for delay. The evidence was that the delay was partly attributable to the client. The Court of Appeal (Salmon LJ) held that 'The liquidated damages and extension of time clauses in printed forms of contract must be construed strictly contra proferentem' and insofar as they appeared to allow the client to benefit from its own wrong (the prevention principle), they could not be read to produce that effect.

Tersons Ltd v Stevenage Development Corporation (1963)

Contractors Tersons undertook certain works in laying sewers for the owner, the Corporation, using the then current General Conditions of Contract. The contractors claimed extra payment for alleged extra or additional work, which the

Corporation, relying on the contract provisions as to variations and payment, said were not to be treated in this way.

The Corporation appealed against the decision of the High Court to overturn the arbitrator's award in their favour. The Court of Appeal dismissed the appeal. Pearson LJ observed that the respondent's counsel had contended that the contra proferentem principle

'... should be applied in this case in favour of the contractor against the Corporation on the ground that the General Conditions were included in the invitation to tender sent by the Corporation to the contractor. In my view the maxim has little, if any application in this case. The General Conditions are not a partisan document or an "imposed standard contract" as that phrase is sometimes used. It was not drawn up by one party in its own interests and imposed on the other party. It is a general form, evidently in common use, and prepared and revised jointly by several representative bodies including the Federation of Civil Engineering Contractors. It would naturally be incorporated in a contract of this kind, and should have the same meaning whether the one party or the other happens to have made the first mention of it in the negotiations.'

Steria Ltd v Sigma Wireless Communications Ltd (2008)

A dispute arose between subcontractor Steria and main contractor Sigma, following delay in the provision of a computerised communications system for emergency services in the Republic of Ireland. Sigma took the point that Steria had failed to comply with the notification requirement for its claim for extension of time. Steria argued that the contra proferentem rule would apply to the words supposedly making notification a condition precedent. Sigma responded that the contra proferentem principle did not apply, as the clause was originally proposed by Steria. The court took a different approach:

'So far as the application of the contra proferentem rule is concerned, it seems to me that the correct question to ask is not whether the clause was put forward originally by

Steria or by Sigma; the principle which applies here is that if there is genuine ambiguity as to whether or not notification is a condition precedent, then the notification should not be construed as being a condition precedent, since such a provision operates for the benefit of only one party ... .'

4.1.2 Invalidity of penalty clauses

The case of *Peak Construction (Liverpool) Ltd v McKinney Foundations Ltd* applied the contra proferentem principle specifically to contractual provisions for liquidated damages and extension of time.

In English law, liquidated damages clauses, if not properly formulated, provide another example of a restriction on the enforceability of whatever the parties have included in their agreement. This is because of the doctrine of penalties, found in English law and a few comparable common law jurisdictions but unknown in many of the world's legal systems.

Most modern construction and engineering contracts, whether standard form or bespoke, contain liquidated damages clauses, whereby an agreed sum is payable by the contractor in the event of late completion or some other breach of contract, such as failure to meet a performance standard. But, as the leading practitioners text, *Keating on Construction Contracts* (8th edition, 2006, p.311) states, 'If the agreed sum, whatever it is called in the contract, is a penalty it will not be enforced by the courts'.

The leading case on this doctrine is still the House of Lords decision in *Dunlop Pneumatic Tyre Co Ltd v New Garage and Motor Co Ltd.* Although it concerned supply of tyres, it is quoted in virtually all the construction cases in which liquidated damages provisions have been challenged as penalties. Lord Dunedin set out the principles governing the distinction and these have been largely applied ever since. The key is that a provision for liquidated damages must be based on a genuine pre-estimate of loss made at the time the contract was entered into, whereas a penalty would be a payment disproportionate to any loss likely to be suffered whose purpose is to discourage breach of contract.

It may be said that this doctrine commands a degree of attention not justified by the number of cases in which contractual provisions have been held unenforceable as penalties. The provisions in the *Dunlop* case itself were upheld. *Arnhold v Attorney-General of Hong Kong* was a case where a clause was held to be a penalty in a major Hong Kong government engineering contract, and in *Jeancharm Ltd v Barnet Football Club Ltd* an interest provision of 260 per cent per annum on late payments was held to be a penalty, but both are unsurprising, or at least explicable on their facts. Apart from these, mainstream authority has remained broadly supportive of liquidated damages clauses and the commercial reasons for doing so were set out by the Privy Council in another Hong Kong case, *Philips Hong Kong Ltd v Attorney General of Hong Kong*. However, while the *Philips* case appeared to emphasise the benefits of liquidated damages provisions and policy reasons why excessive use of the penalty doctrine would not be desirable, it appears not to have changed the law. The Court of Appeal in *Jeancharm v Barnet Football Club* denied that *Philips* had greatly changed the law set out in *Dunlop v New Garage*, which remains largely intact. This is also confirmed by *Alfred McAlpine Capital Projects Ltd v Tilebox Ltd*, which is the most comprehensive recent examination of the case law on liquidated damages and penalties in a construction context. The recent case of *M&J Polymers Lt d v Imerys Minerals Ltd* is an instructive reminder that the penalty doctrine could be applied, as the court confirmed, to breaches of agreement other than late completion, in this case in the context of a take-or-pay agreement; again, the provision was upheld on the facts. Perhaps the single most telling contribution of the case law, apart from the obvious one of setting out the law, is the illustration in the *Alfred McAlpine* case of how parties can avoid uncertainty by being able to refer to the objective evidence (here the minimum weekly rental value), on which the genuine pre-estimate of loss is based. Without such preparatory work, it remains a possibility that a tribunal will refuse to enforce a liquidated damages provision as penal, if it is not satisfied that there has been such a pre-estimate, as there clearly had not in the *Jeancharm* case.

Dunlop Pneumatic Tyre Co Ltd v New Garage and Motor Co Ltd (1915)

Although not a construction case, this decision of the House of Lords is quoted almost invariably whenever the law relating to liquidated damages and penalties is discussed. It arose from contracts for the retail sale by the garage of tyres manufactured by Dunlop, the supplier. The agreement contained provision for the payment of the (then considerable) sum of £5 'for each and every tyre, cover or tube sold or offered in breach of this agreement'. This was expressly stated to be 'by way of liquidated damages and not as a penalty'.

Lord Dunedin's summary of the law is frequently cited in the later cases:

'(i) Though the parties to a contract who use the words "penalty" or "liquidated damages" may *prima facie* be supposed to mean what they say, yet the expression used is not conclusive. The Court must find out whether the payment stipulated is in truth a penalty or liquidated damages. ...

(ii) The essence of a penalty is a payment of money stipulated as *in terrorem* of the offending party; the essence of liquidated damages is a genuine covenanted pre-estimate of damage. ...

(iii) The question whether a sum stipulated is penalty or liquidated damages is a question of construction to be decided upon the terms and inherent circumstances of each particular contract; judged of as at the time of the making of the contract, not as at the time of the breach.'

Lord Dunedin referred to various tests which could prove helpful or conclusive in distinguishing between penalty and liquidated damages.

'(a) It will be held to be a penalty if the sum stipulated for is extravagant and unconscionable in amount in comparison with the greatest loss which could conceivably be proved to have followed from the breach. ...

(b) It will be held to be a penalty if the breach consists only in not paying a sum of money, and the sum stipulated is a sum greater than the sum which ought to have been paid. ...

(c) There is a presumption (but no more) that it is a penalty when "a single lump sum is made payable by way of compensation, on the occurrence of one or more or all of several events, some of which may occasion serious and others but trifling damage". ...

(d) It is no obstacle to the sum stipulated being a genuine pre-estimate of damage that the consequences of the breach are such as to make precise pre-estimation almost an impossibility. On the contrary, that is just the situation when pre-estimated damage was the true bargain between the parties.'

Applying the law to the facts, the House of Lords allowed the appeal and upheld the liquidated damages provision, Lord Parmoor noting that 'the parties had adopted a wise and prudent course, having regard to the nature of the contract and the practical impossibility of an accurate ascertainment of damages'.

Arnhold v Attorney General of Hong Kong (1989)

The contractor on a Hong Kong sewerage works scheme sought to resist the claim by the client, the Hong Kong Government, for liquidated damages for late completion. The High Court of Hong Kong held the liquidated damages clause void as a penalty. The clause provided for a maximum figure of HK$2700 per day. Applying the criteria in *Dunlop Ltd v New Garage Co Ltd*, Sears J held that:

'The figures in this contract are not set out as graduated sums, although they may have that effect. If $2700 per day is the figure for liquidated damages, as is submitted, and this even though it could later be scaled down then, in my judgment, this was the figure which the Government could deduct ... whether there was a delay in the whole of the works, or any portion thereof. The figure may therefore exceed a pre-estimate of damages. If, as I have already set out, the seriousness of the breach would increase the amount of damages, I can find no graduated figures for delay to a portion of the works. Construing this provision, I am of the view that the claim for liquidated damages is a penalty.'

Philips Hong Kong Ltd v Attorney General of Hong Kong (1993)

Philips, as contractor, agreed to supply the Hong Kong Government, the client, with a computerised system for highways and tunnels. The contract contained provision for liquidated damages which varied according to which of the specified Key Dates were not met. Philips obtained declarations that this provision was a penalty but the Hong Kong Court of Appeal overturned this finding. Philips appealed to the Privy Council, which dismissed the appeal. The Privy Council reiterated the test under *Dunlop Pneumatic Tyre Ltd v New Garage Co Ltd* to determine whether contractual provision for liquidated damages is a penalty, namely whether or not it is a genuine pre-estimate of what the loss is likely to be.

Lord Woolf noted that:

'... the Government in its evidence provides an explanation as to how the liquidated damages were calculated. So far as the missing of Key Dates was concerned, the amount of damages was calculated by applying a formula to what was anticipated would be the value of the interfacing contracts. ... In the case of a governmental body the nature of the loss it will suffer as the result of the delay in implementing its new road programme is especially difficult to evaluate. The Government reasonably adopted a formula which reflected the loss of return on the capital involved at a daily rate, to which were added figures for supervisory staff costs, the daily actual cost of making an alternative provision and a sum for fluctuations.'

Lord Woolf criticised

'... the error of assuming that, because in some hypothetical situation the loss suffered will be less than the sum quantified in accordance with the liquidated damages provision, that provision must be a penalty ... . Arguments of this nature should not be allowed to divert attention from the correct test as to what is a penalty provision – namely is it a genuine pre-estimate of what the loss is likely to be? – to the different question, namely are there possible circumstances where a lesser loss would be suffered? Here the minimum payment provision amounted to about 28% of the daily rate of liquidated damages payable for non-completion of the whole works by Philips. The Government point out that if there is delay in completion it will continue inevitably to incur expenses of a standing nature irrespective of the scale of the work outstanding and that those expenses will continue until the work is completed. This being a reasonable assumption and there being no ground for suggesting that the minimum payment limitation was set at the wrong percentage, its presence does not create a penalty.'

Jeancharm Ltd v Barnet Football Club Ltd (2003)

The claimant manufacturer, Jeancharm, had agreed to supply kit to the football club. The supply contract contained provision for interest on late payment at 5 per cent per week, the equivalent of 260 per cent per year. When Jeancharm sought to rely on the interest provision in its claim against Barnet for late payment, the club argued that the provision was a penalty.

Jeancharm's case was that *Philips (Hong Kong) Ltd v Attorney-General of Hong Kong* represented a significant departure from *Dunlop v New Garage*, but this argument was rejected by the Court of Appeal. Jacob J held that:

'... since *Dunlop* the courts have continued to apply the rule in *Dunlop* but have held that one should be careful before deciding whether or not a clause is a penalty when the parties are of equal bargaining power. There was no abandonment of the rule that the clause must be a genuine pre-estimate of damage.'

Keen LJ re-affirmed that the test

'... remains one of ascertaining whether the provision is a genuine pre-estimate of loss or is a penalty for non-performance of the contractual obligation, as was established in *Dunlop* and as *Philips*, more recently, has endorsed .... If one applies that test to the present case, one is bound to conclude that on its face an interest rate of 260% per annum would seem to be penal in nature.'

The football club's appeal was allowed.

Alfred McAlpine Capital Projects Ltd v Tilebox Ltd (2005)

Tilebox, a development company undertaking the refurbishment of a building as a corporate headquarters, engaged Alfred McAlpine as contractors. Tilebox proposed a liquidated damages rate of £45,000 per week, calculated by them as representing the minimum weekly rental value of the completed building. McAlpine had originally objected to this figure as too high, but they agreed it in the contract as executed.

The works were not completed over 2.5 years after the completion date and Tilebox indicated that it would be claiming in respect of all the delay, for which no extension of time would be granted. McAlpine applied for a declaration that the liquidated damages clause was a penalty and therefore invalid. Jackson J in the High Court provided a thorough review of the case law on penalties, including *Dunlop v New Garage* and *Philips v Attorney General of Hong Kong*. He made four general observations on the authorities:

'(1) ... a pre-estimate of damages does not have to be right to be reasonable. There must be a substantial discrepancy between the level of damages stipulated in the contract and the level of damages which is likely to be suffered before it can be said that the agreed pre-estimate is unreasonable.

(2) Although many authorities use or echo the phrase "genuine pre-estimate", the test does not turn upon the genuineness or honesty of the party or parties who made the pre-estimate. The test is primarily an objective one, even though the court has some regard to the thought processes of the parties at the time of contracting.

(3) Because the rule about penalties is an anomaly within the law of contract, the courts are predisposed, where possible, to uphold contractual terms which fix the level of damages for breach. This predisposition is even stronger in the case of commercial contracts freely entered into between parties of comparable bargaining power.

(4) [In the relatively few reported cases] where the relevant clause has been struck down as a penalty ... there was, in fact, a very wide gulf between (a) the level of damages likely to be suffered, and (b) the level of damages stipulated in the contract.'

On the evidence, the liquidated damages provision in the contract 'was an entirely reasonable pre-estimate of damages' and thus not a penalty.

The judge found that the gap between the range of possible weekly losses flowing from delay and the sun of £45,000 'was not nearly wide enough to warrant characterising this clause as a penalty'. Tilebox's director 'did make a genuine attempt to estimate the losses which would flow from future delay'. The difficulty of estimating future losses in this project 'makes it particularly sensible in this case for the parties to have agreed upon a weekly figure'. The court should be 'predisposed where possible to uphold contractual terms which fix the level of damages', especially where, as here, the agreement 'is a commercial contract made between two parties of comparable bargaining power'. It was also relevant that, during negotiations, the parties dealt with this provision specifically and the fact that the proposed figure survived the scrutiny of the parties and their legal advisors was further evidence that it was reasonable. The contractor failed in its attempt to challenge the liquidated damages provision as a penalty.

The following case is a rare, indeed probably unique, authority on take-or-pay clauses as penalties.

M & J Polymers Ltd v Imerys Minerals Ltd (2008)

Under the take-or-pay clause in the supply contract, the buyers committed themselves to buy a minimum quantity of goods, or pay the price of a stipulated minimum if they did not do so. The defendant buyers sought to avoid paying this minimum amount when they failed to order the agreed quantity, on the ground that it was a penalty. The suppliers argued that a take-or-pay clause of this kind could not be a penalty because it was a simple claim in debt for the price of goods. The Commercial Court rejected this wider argument that take-or-pay clauses could not be penalties by definition; the judge declared himself satisfied that 'as a matter of principle, the rule against penalties may apply'. The judge referred to *Dunlop v New Garage*, *Phillips v Attorney General of Hong Kong* and *Alfred McAlpine Capital Projects v Tilebox*, stating that he was

'... entirely satisfied that the take or pay clause was commercially justifiable, did not amount to oppression, was negotiated and freely entered into between parties of comparable bargaining power and did not have the predominant purpose of deterring a breach of contract nor amount to a provision "in terrorem".'

4.1.3 Contractual terms invalidated by statute

The contra proferentem principle and the doctrine of penalties are both common law concepts. It is also possible that contractual provisions agreed by the parties can be invalidated by statute. Three main areas are cited as examples:

- *Unfair Contract Terms Act* 1977;

- *Unfair Terms in Consumer Contracts Regulations* 1999;

- *Housing Grants, Construction and Regeneration Act* 1996 ('HGCRA 1996').

Unfair Contract Terms Act 1977

The most obvious candidate at first sight is the *Unfair Contract Terms Act* 1977. However, its title is misleading, since its application is limited to exclusion and exemption clauses or disclaimers and does not extend to allegedly unfair contract terms more generally. It is certainly possible for purported exclusions of liability to fall foul of the *Unfair Contract Terms Act* 1977, even when the contract has been negotiated to a greater or lesser extent. *Pegler Ltd v Wang (UK) Ltd* is an example of an exclusion clause in a negotiated agreement (although the clause itself was proposed by the supplier) being held to be unreasonable and so contrary to the Act.

However, it would be wrong to suggest that the courts are eager to strike down express terms which have been agreed by the parties, especially if they have negotiated on an equal footing as commercial entities. In *Watford Electronics Ltd v Sanderson Co Ltd*, the Court of Appeal took a restrictive view of the scope for using the *Unfair Contract Terms Act* 1977 to strike down an exclusion clause agreed by two commercial contracting parties. This case appears to be indicative of wider judicial attitudes which are generally supportive of the bargain as made, where consumers are not involved.

Pegler Ltd v Wang (UK) Ltd (2000)

A contract for the supply of computer software, hardware, bespoke programming and services contained the following exclusion clause:

> 'Wang shall not in any event be liable for any indirect, special or consequential loss, howsoever arising (including but not limited to loss of anticipated profits or data) in connection with or arising out of the supply, functioning or use of the hardware, the software or the services even if Wang shall have been advised of the possibility of such potential loss and shall not be liable for any loss except as provided for in this Contract.'

The contract was negotiated between Wang as supplier and Pegler as purchaser, although the exclusion clause was drafted and inserted by Wang.

The court took the view that this clause could not protect Wang against Pegler's claim for lost profits and other damages for breach of contract by Wang. First:

> 'The reference by the words in brackets to loss of anticipated profits does not mean that the exclusion effected by this clause includes all loss of profits: it is plain from the context that only loss of profits which are of the character of indirect, special or consequential loss are referred to.'

Second, the exclusion should be regarded as unreasonable for the purposes of the *Unfair Contract Terms Act* 1997. The Act applied because, so far as the exclusion clause was concerned, Pegler was dealing on Wang's terms, even though the rest of the contract was negotiated. The content of the clause was unreasonable because of the exclusion of liability for breaches highly probable because of the way Wang had misrepresented what it was selling.

Watford Electronics Ltd v Sanderson CFL Ltd (2001)

The contract for supply of software between the purchaser, Watford, and the supplier, Sanderson, contained a provision which purported to exclude liability for direct or consequential loss 'whether arising from negligence or otherwise'. The first instance judge found this unreasonable within the meaning of section 11 of the *Unfair Contract Terms Act* 1977, but the Court of Appeal, allowing the supplier's appeal, upheld the exclusion clause. Unlike those cases which are inevitably limited to their facts or the particular wording of the contract in this one, the Court of Appeal provided a statement of the proper approach to be taken by the courts regarded as setting the tone for the modern law. In the words of Lord Justice Chadwick:

'Where experienced businessmen representing substantial companies of equal bargaining power negotiate an agreement, they may be taken to have had regard to the matters known to them. They should, in my view, be taken to be the best judge of the commercial fairness of the agreement which they have made; including the fairness of each of the terms in that agreement. They should be taken to be the best judge on the question of whether the terms of the agreement are reasonable. The court should not assume that either is likely to commit his company to an agreement which he thinks is unfair, or which he thinks includes unreasonable terms. Unless satisfied that one party has, in effect, taken unfair advantage of the other – or that a term is so unreasonable that it cannot properly have been understood or considered – the court should not interfere.'

The editors of the *Building Law Reports* in which this case is reported observed that:

'Lawyers may have been too willing in the past to raise the 1977 Act as a defence or response to exclusion or limitation clauses. This decision will restrict such pleas.'

Unfair Terms in Consumer Contracts Regulations 1999

The *Unfair Terms in Consumer Contracts Regulations* 1999 also make possible the invalidation of unfair terms, as identified by EU directive. This only applies to consumer contracts, i.e. where the contract concerns a natural person 'acting for purposes which are outside his trade, business or profession'. In construction, attempts have been made to treat the insertion of adjudication provisions in situations which are not within the HGCRA 1996, such as contracts involving residential occupiers, as causing 'a significant imbalance in the parties' rights and obligations arising under the contract, to the detriment of the consumer', under regulation 5(1). Such a result was held to be possible in *Picardi v Cuniberti*, although the actual decision was made on other grounds. Here an architect had failed to draw the adjudication provision in his own conditions of engagement to the client's attention. It should not, though, be regarded as automatic or straightforward. In a number of other cases decided by the Technology and Construction Court (TCC), clients failed to have struck down adjudication provisions in the construction contract, since they or their representatives had imposed them on the contractor, rather than vice versa: *Lovell Projects Ltd v Legg and Carver*, *Westminster Building Co Ltd v Beckingham*, *Bryen & Langley v Martin Boston* and *Allen Wilson Shopfitters v Buckingham*.

Picardi v Cuniberti (2004)

The claimant architect sought a declaration that the contract for professional services with the defendant clients included a version of the RIBA Conditions of Engagement (CE/99) amended to include an adjudication agreement. Because this was a contract concerning a private dwelling house, no adjudication agreement was inserted by the HGCRA 1996. On the facts, the court held that the conditions had not been incorporated into the contract between the parties. However, the judge made some obiter remarks to the effect that the provision would have been invalidated anyway by reason of the *Unfair Terms in Consumer Contracts Regulations* 1999. Regulation 5(1) states that:

> 'A contractual term which has not been individually negotiated shall be regarded as unfair if, contrary to the requirement of good faith, it causes a significant imbalance in the parties' rights and obligations arising under the contract, to the detriment of the consumer.'

HH Judge Toulmin observed that it is

> '... not coincidental that the RIBA guidance clearly requires their members individually to negotiate these clauses. They were right to give such guidance. Mr Picardi did not do so, and if these clauses had been incorporated in his contract with Mr and Mrs Cuniberti, they would be excluded by reason of the Unfair Terms in Consumer Contracts Regulations.'

Lovell Projects Ltd v Legg and Carver (2003)

The claimant, Lovell, the contractor, referred to adjudication a dispute with the employers Mr Legg and Ms Carver, under the *JCT Minor Works Contract*. When the claimant applied for summary judgment of an award in its favour, the defendant argued that the adjudication provisions in the contract created an imbalance between the parties and so should be regarded as an unfair term, following *Picardi v Cuniberti*.

HH Judge Moseley held that there had been no significant imbalance created by the adjudication provision, so that it did not fall foul of the *Unfair Terms in Consumer Contracts Regulations* 1999. He distinguished *Picardi v Cuniberti* where

> 'The client did not have the benefit of any advice concerning the adjudication terms in these provisions: his dispute was with the architect who should have provided that advice. ... None of the relevant terms had been drawn to the client's attention let alone specifically negotiated.'

Judge Moseley said that he would

> '... accept entirely the correctness of that decision, but it has no application to a case where the form of contract was insisted on by the employers, who had available both advice from solicitors and from their nominated contract administrator.

> For those reasons in my judgment the employers in the present case were bound by the adjudication terms in their contract with the contractor. Those terms are not struck down by the 1999 Regulations.'

Westminster Building Co Ltd v Beckingham (2004)

The defendant clients, Beckingham, entered into a contract with the claimant contractor, Westminster, for refurbishment work to a private dwelling house. A dispute was referred to adjudication under provision in the *JCT Intermediate Form of Contract* used. The claimant sought enforcement of the decision in its favour. The defendant argued that the adjudication provision was unenforceable as contrary to the *Unfair Terms in Consumer Contracts Regulations* 1999. HH Judge Thornton in the TCC applied *Lovell Projects Ltd v Legg and Carver* in finding that the provision was not unfair. It was 'couched in plain and intelligible language', was accepted on the basis of 'competent and objective advice' as to its existence and effect and did not 'constitute a significant imbalance' in the client's rights vis-à-vis the contractor. *Picardi v Cuniberti* was not cited.

Bryen & Langley v Martin Boston (2005)

Bryen & Langley, the claimant contractors, referred to adjudication a dispute arising from refurbishment works carried out to the home of the defendant client, Boston. The client argued that the adjudication provision in the JCT 98 contract was unfair within the meaning of the *Unfair Terms in Consumer Contracts Regulations* 1999. The Court of Appeal, allowing an appeal on other grounds from the TCC, gave guidance on how the Regulations should be applied to such clauses:

> '... in assessing whether a term that has not been individually negotiated is "unfair" for the purposes of Regulation 5(1), it is necessary to consider not merely the commercial effects of the term on the relative rights of the parties but, in particular, whether the term has been imposed on the consumer in circumstances which justify a conclusion that the supplier has fallen short of the requirements of fair dealing. The situation at which Regulation 5(1) is directed is one in which the supplier, who will normally be presumed to be in a stronger bargaining position, has imposed a standard-form contract on the consumer containing terms which are, or might be said to be, loaded unfairly in favour of the supplier.

> ... Mr Boston faces exactly the same difficulty in relation to his Regulation 5(1) argument as did the consumers in the *Lovell* and *Beckingham* cases. His problem is that the relevant provisions were not imposed upon him by B&L (the supplier). It was Mr Boston (the consumer), acting through his agent ... who imposed them on the supplier, since they were specified in (the) original invitation to tender ... if they were to tender at all, B&L were being asked by Mr Boston to tender on (inter alia) the very terms of which Mr Boston now complains. It was not for B&L to take the matter up with him and ensure that he knew what he was doing: they knew that he had the benefit of the

services of a professional ... to advise him of the effects of the terms on which he was inviting tenders ... there was no lack of openness, fair dealing or good faith in the manner in which the ... contract came to be made.'

(See also section 3.1 on letters of intent/award/appointment on this case.)

Allen Wilson Shopfitters v Buckingham (2005)

The claimant contractors had carried out work on the defendant client's property and referred a dispute to adjudication. The defendant, resisting enforcement by way of summary judgment, argued that the adjudication provisions in the contract were unfair within the *Unfair Terms in Consumer Contract Regulations* 1999. HH Judge Coulson rejected this argument, relying on *Westminster Building Co Ltd v Beckingham* and *Bryen & Langley Ltd v Boston*. *Picardi v Cuniberti* was distinguished:

'... one of the principal reasons why the learned judge came to the view that, if there had been an adjudication agreement, it may have offended against the Regulations, was because the proposed adjudication agreement in that case had been originally put forward by the claimant architect, so that, if he had been able to establish the contract for which he contended, he could then have relied upon that agreement.'

Housing Grants, Construction and Regeneration Act 1996

The 1996 Act itself, as well as being capable of inserting provisions into contracts, can also invalidate certain terms. One of its most-heralded achievements was in making ineffective, under section 113, pay-when-paid clauses which are 'conditional upon the payer receiving payment from a third party'. In *Midland Expressway Ltd v Carillion Construction Ltd*, the TCC held invalid a so-called 'pay-when-certified' provision commonly used in PFI (private finance initiative) projects, on the ground that it was only a variation on the proscribed 'pay-when-paid' theme and not something intrinsically different. Note that, at the time of writing, the Construction Contracts Bill 2008 is before Parliament. Its amendments to the

1996 Act include widening the categories of payment mechanism made invalid on the same basis as 'pay-when-paid' clauses.

Midland Expressway Ltd v Carillion Construction Ltd (2005)

The claimant concessionaire, Midland Expressway, had been granted by the government the concession for designing, constructing and operating the Birmingham Northern Relief Road as a toll road. The defendants were a construction joint venture, the contractors, CAMBBA. A provision of the contract between Midland and CAMBBA restricted any price adjustment in CAMBBA's favour to the amounts which Midland was entitled to be paid under its concession agreement. One of the points taken in the claim by Midland to prevent CAMBBA referring an interim payment dispute to adjudication was that CAMBBA could not proceed with its claim until Midland's entitlement under the concession agreement was ascertained.

Section 113 of the HGCRA 1996 provides that 'A provision making payment under a construction contract conditional upon the payer receiving payment from a third person is ineffective ...' (with the exception of insolvency of the third person or other debtor).

Jackson J held that:

> 'The practical consequence of clause 39.6.2 is that CAMBBA will not be paid for department's changes unless and until MEL has received a corresponding sum from the department. This is so even in cases where CAMBBA has established or could establish an entitlement to payment under the dispute resolution procedures of the [Design & Construct] contract. This state of affairs is precisely what s.113 of the 1996 Act is legislating against.

> Clause 39.6.2 uses the phrase "the amounts ... to which the employer is entitled to be paid" rather than "the amounts which the employer is paid". In my view, this particular choice of language cannot save the clause. Contracting parties cannot escape the operation of s.113 by the use of circumlocution. ...

... it may be surprising that the parties have used any contractual provisions which are ineffective under the 1996 Act. There is, however, an explanation for this ... . The [Design & Construct] contract is based on PFI contract forms. PFI contracts are outside the scope of the 1996 Act. Therefore PFI contract forms have not been drafted with a view to compliance with those provisions.'

4.2 RECTIFICATION

As should be apparent from the aggregated content of section 4, the parties cannot be said to have absolute control over the substance of their agreement, although they can retain a much higher degree of control if they avoid the respective pitfalls of the contra proferentem principle, the penalty doctrine and legislation which invalidates certain types of clause. It is desirable briefly to consider what course of action is available if the contract does not accurately reflect the parties' agreement. Apart from replacing it by mutual consent, which is possible if the parties are prepared to cooperate to deal with a perceived problem, there may be scope for a party to apply to the court for rectification, i.e. changing the record of the agreement to reflect what it should have said. As the editors of the *Building Law Reports* put it in their commentary on *George Wimpey UK Ltd v VIC Construction Ltd*:

'Rectification is an equitable remedy and by its very nature, particularly in relation to unilateral mistakes, is applied only with great caution.'

The *George Wimpey* case is useful because the Court of Appeal, in allowing the appeal against the grant of rectification, set out the requirements which would have to be met.

However, while the requirements are exacting, a court may be prepared to exercise its discretion, especially where there is unconscionable conduct, such as in the case of *Hurst Stores Ltd v ML Europe Property Ltd*, where the party introducing a change into the document from that negotiated had probably 'wilfully shut his eyes' to the possibility of misapprehension by the other party. Rectification was accordingly granted.

George Wimpey UK Ltd v VIC Construction Ltd (2005)

VIC Construction, a developer, sold land to Wimpey for residential construction. The contract provided for a lump sum payment by Wimpey, followed by further payments based on a formula dependent on Wimpey's total sales proceeds from the development. After protracted negotiations, the payment formula was agreed, but reference to enhancements was omitted in error from the document drafted by VIC's professional adviser. Wimpey commenced proceedings subsequently, claiming rectification of the agreement, alleging both common mistake and unilateral mistake.

The first instance judge ordered rectification, but the Court of Appeal allowed VIC's appeal. The court stated the requirements for rectification in cases of unilateral mistake as follows:

(i)   Party A must erroneously believe that the document contained a particular term or provision (or possibly must believe that it did not when it did).

(ii)   Party B must be aware of the error and that it arose from Party A's mistake.

(iii)   Party B must have omitted to draw the mistake to Party A's attention.

(iv)   The mistake must be calculated to benefit Party B.

This represented a high level to meet in order to succeed in a claim for rectification and, on the facts, VIC fell short. As Lord Justice Peter Gibson put it:

'I recognise that the mistake has had serious consequences for Wimpey and brought a benefit to VIC which it did not foresee in putting forward the formula. But that is not determinative of whether Wimpey can successfully invoke the exceptional jurisdiction to rectify for unilateral mistake.'

Hurst Stores Ltd v ML Europe Property Ltd (2003), (2004)

A contractor's representative signed a statement of account into which the employer's representative had inserted the words 'in full and final settlement'. The contractor sought rectification of the statement document on the basis of unilateral mistake. The first instance judge found that the probability was that the employer's representative was 'wilfully shutting his eyes' to the risk that the contractor's representative 'would not notice the newly introduced, potentially prejudicial words which he had no reason to suspect might be there' and failed to take reasonable steps, knowing 'that the document he had prepared did not simply reflect the agreement … which had been reached earlier that month after protracted negotiations. For these reasons, in my judgment the 27 April document 2001 should be rectified by deleting the paragraphs which I have identified'. The Court of Appeal upheld the finding of the TCC on rectification and also on the other issues appealed.

4.3 IMPLIED TERMS

Section 4.1 dealt with cases where a provision expressly agreed might be invalidated by operation of a rule of common law or of statutory provision. The mirror image is considered in this section, namely that clauses may be inserted into the agreement which were not expressly agreed by the parties. These implied terms may also result from statute or common law. The examples given are divided into:

- terms implied by statute;
- terms implied by common law.

4.3.1 TERMS IMPLIED BY STATUTE

The examples given of terms implied by statute are divided into:

- sale of goods and defective premises;
- *Housing Grants, Construction and Regeneration Act* 1996.

Sale of goods and defective premises

The supply of materials by a manufacturer to a contractor or subcontractor will normally constitute a sale of goods and so the contract would be subject to the *Sale of Goods Act* 1979 as amended. Note that a typical construction contract would not comprise a sale of goods, as was made clear in *Rotherham MBC v Frank Haslam Milan*, although a common law implied term was substituted. There is often great similarity between basic statutory implied terms and their common law counterparts. Thus in *Hancock v Brazier Ltd*, the Court of Appeal held that a builder of a house impliedly warrants that his materials are good and proper materials, the work is done in a good and workmanlike manner and the end product, the house, is fit for human habitation. The *Defective Premises Act 1972*, section 1(1) provides that the duty of 'A person taking on work for or in connection with the provision of a dwelling' is 'to see that the work which he takes on is done in a workmanlike or, as the case may be, professional manner, with proper materials and so that as regards that work the dwelling will be fit for habitation when completed'.

The problem with reliance on implied terms as to quality, rather than express terms tailored to the specific purpose of the owner/client, is that their adequacy is not easy to assess at the procurement stage. In both *Rotherham MBC v Frank Haslam Milan* and *Jewson v Boykan*, a term as to merchantable (*Rotherham*) and satisfactory (*Jewson*) quality was implied but not breached on the facts, while no warranty as to fitness for purpose was implied, due to failure of the client/purchaser to articulate its purpose adequately.

Rotherham MBC v Frank Haslam Milan & Co Ltd (1996)

Rotherham MBC, the client, engaged FHM as contractors for site preparation and foundation work including the supply and laying of imported fill material as part of the construction of new council offices. Steel slag was used as granular fill, which expanded, causing heave, cracking the reinforced concrete foundation slabs. Rotherham sued the contractors for breach of implied terms as to merchantable quality and fitness for purpose of the steel slag.

At first, as the Court of Appeal noted, it had been

> '... originally pleaded that each of the contracts was subject to implied terms under s.14(2) and (3) of the Sale of Goods Act 1979. But when the point was taken that there were no sales of goods but only contracts for work and materials Rotherham were permitted to add in relation to

each implied term the alternative allegations that corresponding terms were to be implied at common law.'

In the circumstances, the Court of Appeal did not allow the implication at common law of the fitness for purpose term. The term as to merchantability was implied by common law, although on the facts it had not been breached; the steel slag was quite saleable i.e. merchantable, it was just unsuitable for the specific purpose.

Note that section 14(2) of the *Sale of Goods Act* 1979 was amended by the *Sale and Supply of Goods Act* 1994 so that it now reads 'where the seller sells goods in the course of a business, there is an implied term that the goods supplied under the contract are of satisfactory quality'. The requirement of 'merchantable quality' was removed from the statute and replaced by 'satisfactory quality'.

Hancock v BW Brazier (Anerley) Ltd (1966)

The defendant builders were sued by the purchasers of one of their houses when the foundations cracked. The builders had used hard-core containing sodium sulphate which absorbed water, causing the cracking. The Court of Appeal held that a builder owed a three-fold warranty under an implied term when constructing a house: to do his work in a good and workmanlike manner, to use good and proper materials and that the house will be reasonably fit for human habitation. As Lord Denning said of the materials:

> 'The quality of the materials is left to be implied; and the necessary implication is that they should be good and suitable for the work. I am quite clear that it is implied in the contract that the hardcore must be good and proper hardcore, in the same way as the bricks must be good and proper bricks.'

Note that the three-fold implied terms were imported into statute in section 1(1) of the *Defective Premises Act* 1972.

Jewson Ltd v Boykan (2004)

An occasional property developer purchased electric boilers from Jewson for a 13-unit development of flats. All worked satisfactorily, but the developer had difficulty selling the flats because the boilers did not meet the energy Standard Assessment Procedure criteria. When Jewsons sued for the price of the boilers, they were met with a counterclaim based on breach of section 14(2) and (3) of the *Sale of Goods Act* 1979 as amended, which was upheld by the first instance judge. On appeal by Jewsons, the Court of Appeal held that the supplier had given insufficient information on his specific purpose to be able to rely upon a fitness for purpose implied term. A term as to satisfactory quality under section 14(2) would be implied, but had not been breached on the facts.

Housing Grants, Construction and Regeneration Act 1996

In English construction law (there are similar provisions in place in Scotland), the most significant impact by statute upon the contents of construction contracts was introduced by the HGCRA 1996, which came into effect in 1998. At the time of writing, a draft Construction Contracts Bill had just been published, scheduled to go before Parliament in December 2008, with the presumed intention of introduction in 2009.

The HGCRA 1996, as well as invalidating certain provisions (see pay-when-paid clauses and *Midland Expressway v Carillion* above), also requires the presence of key elements in a construction contract (as defined by the HGCRA 1996) and inserts them if they are absent. They are not always referred to as implied terms, but that is what they are in effect.

These elements are of two kinds and are dealt with as:

- payment provisions;
- adjudication.

Both have led to a significant number of reported cases, especially the latter, for which see the *Construction Adjudication* title in the *Case in Point* series, by Richard Mills. A small number of examples are here considered sufficient for illustrative purposes.

Payment provisions

The mechanism by which the statutory implication takes place under the HGCRA 1996 is the Scheme for Construction Contracts, a statutory instrument made by delegated powers under the HGCRA 1996 and coming into force in May 1998. Thus Part II of the Scheme provides that 'Where the parties to a relevant construction contract fail to agree' the payment provisions required by the HGCRA 1996, the relevant provisions of the Scheme apply.

In *C&B Scene Concept Design Ltd v Isobars Ltd* and the Scottish case of *Karl Construction (Scotland) Ltd v Sweeney Civil Engineering (Scotland) Ltd*, it was held that the inadequacy of the parties' contractual provision for interim payments meant that Part II of the Scheme would be applied to ascertain the position between them instead.

C&B Scene Concept Design Ltd v Isobars Ltd (2002)

C&B, the claimant contractor on a cafe refurbishment, referred to adjudication three interim payment applications unpaid by Isobars, the employer. The parties had failed to select either of the interim payment options under the (*JCT 88*) contract and the first instance judge held Isobars entitled to deny that the claims were due, even though it had failed to give notice in accordance with the contract. The Court of Appeal upheld this finding (per Sir Stuart Murray-Smith):

> 'In the absence of contractual provisions as to how much should be paid by interim payments and when that payment should be made, the provisions of s.109 of the Housing Grants Construction and Regeneration Act 1996 … came into play so as to imply the relevant provisions of the Scheme for Construction Contracts (England and Wales) Regulations 1998 … .'

In the result, C&B's appeal was, however, allowed, because the error of law by the adjudicator had not been sufficient to deprive him of jurisdiction.

Karl Construction (Scotland) Ltd v Sweeney Civil Engineering (Scotland) Ltd (2000)

Subcontractors Sweeney referred to adjudication an interim payment dispute with main contractors Karl, on the basis of failure by Karl to respond to interim payment applications. Karl took the point that in the adjudication Sweeney had failed to establish any contractual entitlement and sought judicial review of the adjudicator's decision.

Lord Caplan in the Court of Session (Outer House) found that the adjudicator was entitled to conclude that the sub-contract contained no adequate mechanism for deciding when an interim payment became due and that it was then open to her to fall back on the Scheme to make a finding that Sweeney was entitled to payment:

> 'Once she decides that the Sub-Contract in fact contains no adequate mechanism for deciding when instalment payments become due, her knowledge of Part II of the Scheme is no doubt sufficient to permit her to make a finding that in the circumstances Sweeney were entitled to the redress they have claimed in the adjudication.'

Note that this decision of the Court of Session, Outer House was upheld by the Inner House on other grounds in January 2002.

Adjudication provisions

As with the payment provisions under the HGCRA 1996, missing or non-compliant adjudication provisions can be replaced by the provisions under the Scheme. In *John Mowlem Ltd v Hydra-tight Ltd*, the judge considered whether any compliant parts of the adjudication provisions might survive by being severed from the non-compliant provisions. The conclusion was that they could not: either the provisions for adjudication comply, or the Scheme provisions operate. In *Epping Electrical Co Ltd v Briggs and Forrester (Plumbing Services) Ltd* and *Aveat Heating Ltd v Jerram Falkus Construction Ltd*, the effect of this created a considerable impact in the construction industry. Contracting parties who had adopted widely-used standard form provisions – in *Epping* the CIC Model Adjudication procedure and in *Aveat* the GC/Works Subcontract, found that these were substituted as being non-compliant and the Scheme provisions implied in their place.

John Mowlem Ltd v Hydra-tight Ltd (2001)

Subcontractor Hydra-tight sought to refer to adjudication an interim payment dispute with the main contractor, Mowlem. The subcontract contained an adjudication clause, but with provision for deferral for four weeks of referral to adjudication, pending the service of a 'notice of dissatisfaction'. Mowlem applied for a declaration that the adjudicator had no jurisdiction.

His Honour Judge Toulmin held that:

'Section 108 of the Act provides for a right to refer a dispute to adjudication and a mechanism by which it is to be achieved. …

Section 108(1) provides: "A party to a construction contract has the right to refer a dispute arising under the contract for adjudication under a procedure complying with this section."

Section 108(5) provides "If the contract does not comply with the requirements of subsections (1) to (4) the adjudication provisions of the Scheme for Construction Contracts apply."

This contract does not comply with [the subsections] since … the parties have no immediate right to refer at any time or to give notice of an intention to refer a dispute to adjudication.

… I accept the argument that [the contract] does not provide a timetable for the securing of the appointment of an adjudicator and referral of a dispute to him within seven days. Therefore, on the plain wording of the statute, the Scheme applies.

I have considered whether, if some parts of the subcontract comply with the Act, they can be retained and the Act can be used in substitution for or to fill in those parts of the subcontract which are contrary to the Act. But the words of the Act are clear. Either a party complies in its own terms and conditions with the requirements of sections 108(1) to (4) of the Act or the provisions of the Scheme apply.'

Aveat Heating Ltd v Jerram Falkus Construction Ltd (2007)

The claimant subcontractor undertook to perform plumbing and mechanical works for the defendant subcontractor on a residential estate, using the GC/Works Subcontract conditions. The claimant obtained an adjudication decision and sought enforcement of it. The defendant argued that the terms of the subcontract were non-compliant with the HGCRA 1996 because of the time limits for referral and notification of decision by the adjudicator. Applying John *Mowlem Ltd v Hydra-Tight Ltd* and *Epping Electrical Co Ltd v Briggs and Forrester (Plumbing Services) Ltd*, His Honour Judge Richard Havery QC held that the effect was that the Scheme for Construction Contracts should supplant the contract provisions:

> 'It is true that the Act does not say that if the Scheme applies, the contractual adjudication provisions are void. But if they are not void, the contract contains competing and to some extent mutually contradictory provisions. One could then make sense of the contract only if, in the case of every pair of mutually contradictory provisions, only one member of the pair were to be treated in any given case as prevailing over the other. I unhesitatingly follow Judge Toulmin [in *John Mowlem Ltd v Hydra-Tight Ltd*] in reaching the conclusion that that is not the intention … .
>
> In my judgment, the Scheme and the contractual provisions cannot coexist in the contract unless provision is made in the contract how that is to work. …
>
> I conclude that the Scheme was implied into the contract in place of clause 38A.'

Epping Electrical Co Ltd v Briggs and Forrester (Plumbing Services) Ltd (2007)

Epping was sub-subcontractor to Briggs, subcontractor on a London residential development. Disputes were referred to adjudication, for which provision under the Construction Industry Council (CIC) Model Adjudication procedure was made in the contract. Briggs sought to resist enforcement of the adjudicator's award on the ground that the time-limits for the adjudicator's decision were non-compliant with the HGCRA 1996. His Honour Judge Havery QC held that the provision of the CIC Model Adjudication procedure, by which the adjudicator's decision could be valid after the agreed date for making it, was inconsistent with section 108(2) of the Act, which requires the adjudicator to reach a decision within a stated time limit or agreed extended time:

'The apparent effect of para 25 of the CIC procedure is inconsistent with the mandatory nature of section 108(2) and the apparently mandatory nature of paras 16 and 24 are effectively non-mandatory and the contract does not comply with section 108(2) of the Act, so the Scheme applies. In my judgment, para 25 cannot then survive. The Scheme applies in place of the adjudication provisions of the contract.'

4.3.2 Terms implied by common law

Certain of the most basic implied terms developed by common law have been incorporated into statute. Thus the builder of a dwelling house, who under *Hancock v Brazier* gave a three-fold implied warranty as to quality of workmanship, quality of materials and fitness of the house for human habitation, now has a similar obligation under the *Defective Premises Act* 1972 (see above). Such basic terms are difficult to exclude without the potential difficulties created by the *Unfair Contract Terms Act* 1977 and the contra proferentem principle.

But in general terms it is not the function of the common law to improve contracts or to make additions on the ground that they are reasonable, as the House of Lords made clear in *Trollope & Colls v North West Metropolitan Regional Hospital Board*.

Implied terms can, however, be varied by context. The usual implied term under section 13 of the *Supply of Goods and Services Act* 1982 is that a construction (or other) professional will supply its service with reasonable care and skill under the so-called *Bolam* principle (from the medical case *Bolam v Friern Hospital Management Committee*). So a professional engineer would typically owe such a duty to its client/employer for design services, either expressly through its conditions of engagement or, in their absence, by implication. However, in *Greaves (Contractors) Ltd v Baynham Meikle & Partners*, the court was concerned with the engineer's duty to the design and build contractor who was its client, the contractor having accepted a duty to the owner to ensure that the building, including the design, was fit for its purpose. These circumstances were sufficient to change the implied duty of the engineer from 'reasonable care and skill' to 'fitness for purpose'. Some of Lord Denning's statements in that case might appear to contradict the House of Lords' statements in *Trollope & Colls v North West Metropolitan Regional Hospital Board*, to the effect that courts will not improve the bargain beyond what was intended or is necessary to make sense, but the Court of Appeal indicated that the parties had really shown intention in their communications and behaviour, so the finding was based on the facts of this case, albeit that they will be quite common in design and build projects.

Trollope & Colls v North West Metropolitan Regional Hospital Board (1973)

Contracts between the contractors and the Board for construction work contained provision for phased completion of separate elements of the project. A delay on Phase 1 left the contractors only 16 months instead of the anticipated 30 months to complete Phase 3, and they called upon the Board's architects to nominate subcontractors who could achieve this. The Board failed to find subcontractors to do so and argued that the contract should be read to include an implied extension of time, even though the contractors had not sought one. The contractors, by agreement, commenced proceedings for a declaration that no such implied extension of time should be granted, so that they would not be bound by the contract prices agreed. The Board wished to save the contractual provisions by implying the extension of time necessary to make completion possible.

The first instance judge gave judgment for the contractors, but the Court of Appeal found for the Board. The House of Lords allowed the contractors' appeal and gave an important statement on the general principles applicable to the implication of terms: Lord Pearson referred to 'the basic principle that the court does not make a contract for the parties'. This was expanded upon:

> 'The court will not even improve the contract which the parties have made for themselves, however desirable the improvement might be. The court's function is to interpret and apply the contract which the parties have made for themselves. If the express terms are perfectly clear and free from ambiguity, there is no choice to be made between different possible meanings: the clear terms must be applied even if the court thinks some other terms would

have been more suitable. An unexpressed term can be implied if and only if the court finds that the parties have intended that term to form part of their contract; it is not enough for the court to find that such a term would have been adopted by the parties as reasonable men if it had been suggested to them: it must have been a term that went without saying, a term necessary to give business efficacy to the contract, a term which, though tacit, formed part of the contract which the parties made for themselves.'

The alleged extension of time 'is not obviously what the parties must have intended and, therefore, is not to be implied'.

Greaves (Contractors) Ltd v Baynham Meikle & Partners (1975)

The plaintiff design and build contractors had undertaken to produce a warehouse and offices for the client, an oil business, which would use the warehouse for storing barrels of oil. The floors cracked because of vibration from the loaded fork-lift trucks in the warehouse. The contractors, being liable to their client for failure to produce a building fit for its purpose, claimed against the structural engineers they had engaged for the design. The engineers appealed against the finding of the trial judge against them, arguing that they had only undertaken to use the normal 'reasonable care and skill' of a professional, which they had not failed to do.

Lord Denning MR and the Court of Appeal dismissed this argument and the appeal:

'It has often been stated that the law will only imply a term when it is reasonable and necessary to do so in order to give business efficacy to the transaction; and, indeed so obvious that both parties must have intended it. But those statements must be taken with considerable qualification. In the great majority of cases it is no use looking for the intention of both parties. ... So the courts imply – or as I would say, impose – a term such as is just and reasonable in the circumstances.'

While, in the case of a professional, 'The law does not usually imply a warranty that he will achieve the desired result, but only a term that he will use reasonable care and skill', here the circumstances were different:

> '... the evidence shows that both parties were of one mind on the matter. Their common intention was that the engineer should design a warehouse which would be fit for the purpose for which it was required. That common intention gives rise to a term implied in fact. ... there was implied in fact a term that, if the work was completed in accordance with the design, it would be reasonably fit for the use of loaded stacker-trucks. The engineers failed to make such a design and are, therefore, liable.'

Contractors are, in any event, routinely under a fitness for purpose duty, often expressly, but if not, then by reason of a common law implied term. Examples can be found in *Wilson v Wallace, Consultants Group International v Worman (John)* and *Viking Grain Storage Ltd v TH White Installations Ltd*, in all of which the construction contract was construed to include a fitness for purpose duty.

Wilson v Wallace (1859)

The clients had requested the contractor to quote prices for the supply of metal tanks to certain specifications: that they should be 2 feet 8 inches square and 4½ inches deep with quarter-inch plates and a stay or bolt through the centre; each to stand a head pressure of 60 inches of water. Three holes would be inserted in a place to be pointed out. The contractor claimed for the costs of executing the work in a particular way, notably inserting an extra stay, which the contractor argued constituted an extra. The Lord President rejected the contractor's claim, holding that he was under an implied duty to achieve fitness for purpose: the contractor

> '... did nothing more than was necessary to make these tanks of the quality power and strength necessary to sustain the pressure that he was told was to be upon them and which by the general words of the contract he was bound to make them capable of sustaining. If anything for that purpose was required to be done that was not in the specification, it was the pursuer's duty to supply it.'

Consultants Group International v Worman (John) (1985)

The case concerned the construction of an abattoir and the extent of the implied duty of fitness for purpose. The judge held that the contract should be interpreted:

> '... not only to make it workable, but also to give effect to what I regard as the indisputable object of the whole bargain, which was not merely to produce an abattoir that would work to scheduled capacity, but which would also achieve the necessary standards for UK and EEC financial aid.'

It should be noted that there was express reference in the contract to compliance with EEC standards; the point is that any individual design obligation has to be read in the context of that overall requirement.

Viking Grain Storage Ltd v TH White Installations Ltd (1985)

In this case, it was regarded as well established that, where the client relies on the contractor for design as well as construction, an implied duty of fitness for purpose exists. HH Judge Davies was clear that

> '... such a term is to be implied in this case. The purpose of the contract was so obvious as not to need stating. It was equally obvious that Viking needed a granary which would be reasonably fit to handle 10,000 tons by one-man operation. Did they rely on White's skills and judgement to do so? Of course they did. ... The whole point of engaging White was to rely on White's expertise and experience in the field of designing and constructing granaries. I find it impossible to differentiate between the reliance placed by Viking on White with regard to the quality of the materials and their design, the design and specifications of the functional part of the installation as a whole, and the condition of the ground. All these things were integral and independent parts of the whole.'

As the *Greaves v Baynham Meikle* case demonstrates, what terms, if any, are implied into the agreement the parties have made depends upon the circumstances, including any expressions of intention or understanding. So, while the courts' reticence if invited to intervene to improve a contract or save a party from a bad bargain remains intact, the variety of *possible* implied terms is very wide. It is therefore literally impossible to canvass every conceivable implied term. It is not particularly useful to do so, if the facts leading to the implication are 'one-offs'. One reason (of several) for inclusion of *Greaves v Baynham Meikle* is that, while the Court of Appeal referred to it as dependent on its facts, they are relatively common in design and build contracting. Unless the designer has been able to insist upon terms of engagement with the contractor which expressly refer to 'reasonable care and skill', as do the standard form conditions produced by professional bodies such as RIBA, a duty to achieve fitness for purpose of design may well be implied into the agreement. The impact upon the designer's risk exposure need not be given any more emphasis; it may, of course, extend to affecting professional indemnity insurance cover, which is usually restricted to basic reasonable care and skill liability.

Contractors would not be normally taken aback by an implied term of fitness for purpose, but where implication of less well-known terms becomes a judicial trend, there is cause for concern. A good example is the contractor's 'duty to warn'. This means, in effect, that in certain circumstances, a contractor may be under a duty to detect and warn against errors in design even under a traditional procurement arrangement. This extension of the law has been entirely achieved by implication of terms, beginning with the Supreme Court of Canada's decision in *Brunswick Construction v Nowlan* and developing in the UK through *EDAC v William Moss, Victoria University of Manchester v Hugh Wilson* and most recently *Plant Construction plc v Clive Adam Associates*, although the limits of implication were re-stated in *University of Glasgow v William Whitfield*.

Before concluding these examples of common law implied terms, it should be noted that they can involve obligations by clients/employers as well as contractors, subcontractors and consultants. Thus in *London Borough of Merton v Stanley Hugh Leach Ltd*, there was held to be an implied term that the local authority, the client, would not hinder or prevent the contractor's execution of its work and discharge of its obligations.

Brunswick Construction Ltd v Nowlan (1974)

The client obtained a house design from an architect, who played no further part in the project. The client gave the design to Brunswick, as contractor, to build it. The structure failed, due to a roof design defect. The trial judge exonerated the contractor, but on appeal the contractor was held liable. In a ground-breaking judgment, the Supreme Court of Canada held the contractor to be in breach of an implied duty 'to warn the respondents/clients of the danger inherent in executing the architect's plans'.

Equitable Debenture Assets Corp v Moss (1984)

EDAC, the clients, were the developers of an office block. The building, in an exposed position, suffered weather penetration from the first day of its life – during construction and after it, due to defective curtain walling. The problem was the specification of the sealant. EDAC sued their architects, curtain walling consultants and sub-contractors, but this note solely concerns judgment against the main contractors.

HH Judge Newey QC held that it must have become apparent during the course of the work that the curtain walling design was unbuildable and they should have reported it to the client or its advisors:

> '... in order to give efficacy to the contract the term requiring Moss to warn of design defects as soon as they came to believe that they existed was to be implied into the contract.'

Victoria University of Manchester v Hugh Wilson (1984)

Following the failure of the cladding of its reinforced concrete building, the University sued its contractor (its architects settled the claim against them). The judge held that the contractors were under a duty, following *EDAC v William Moss*, to warn of the design deficiency:

> '... a term was to be implied into each contract requiring the contractors to warn the architects as the University's agents of defects in design, which they believed to exist.

Belief that there were defects required more than mere doubt as to the correctness of the design, but less than actual knowledge of errors.'

Plant Construction plc v Clive Adams Associates and JMH Construction Services Ltd (2000)

Plant was employed by Ford Motor Co as design and build contractor on works at Ford's research centre. Plant engaged JMH as subcontractor for substructure works. JMH was given instruction by Ford's engineer on temporary works design, which JMH queried. JMH proceeded with the design and the temporary works collapsed. Ford claimed against Plant for damage done and other costs and received £1.3 million in settlement. Plant claimed against Clive Adams, its consultant engineers (who settled) and JMH.

Lord Justice May in the Court of Appeal, citing *Brunswick Construction v Nowlan*, *EDAC v William Moss*, *Victoria University of Manchester v Hugh Wilson* and *University of Glasgow v William Whitfield*, held that JMH's implied obligation carried with it a duty to warn of the danger they perceived.

> 'Any analysis of implied terms in a building contract must start with and take proper account of its express terms. Subject to the express terms, there will normally be an implied term that the contractor will perform his contract with the skill and care of an ordinarily competent contractor in the circumstances of the actual contractor. ... the factual extent of the performance which this term requires will depend on all relevant circumstances, which may vary enormously. ... JMH, with others, had a duty to guard against the risk of personal injury to a potentially large number of people. That duty extended to giving proper warnings about the risk. It was not itself a contractual duty owed to Plant, but it is a relevant circumstance in determining the extent of the performance which JMH's implied duty of skill and care required.'

In the result, JMH had breached this duty by proceeding to implement an obviously flawed and dangerous design with insufficient warning or protest.

University of Glasgow v William Whitfield and John Lang Construction Ltd (1988)

The University employed contractors to build an art gallery. When the building failed, suffering water ingress, they sued their architects. The architects joined the contractors, alleging that the contractors should have warned both architects and clients of design defects.

HH Judge Bowsher distinguished *EDAC v William Moss* and *Victoria University of Manchester v Hugh Wilson* on their facts in finding that:

> '... where there is a detailed contract of the nature found here, there is no room for the implication of a duty to warn about possible defects in design'

although the judge wished to

> '... make it plain that I am not saying that there are no circumstances in which a term may be implied or a duty owed in tort requiring a contractor to warn a building owner of defects in the design.'

London Borough of Merton v Stanley Hugh Leach Ltd (1986)

Leach, the contractor, contended that the substantial delay in completing 287 dwellings for Merton, as employer, was almost wholly due to Merton's fault, including lack of co-operation. Leach obtained an arbitration award in its favour on loss and expense and extension of time, which Merton sought to challenge. One of a large number of issues concerned the implication of a term that the employer, either directly or through its architect, would not hinder the contractor's timely execution of its contractual obligations.

Vinelott J gave judgment for Leach on this point:

> 'Vaughan Williams LJ observed in *Barque Quilpue Ltd* v. *Brown* (1904): "There is an implied contract by each party that he will not do anything to prevent the other party from performing a contract or to delay him in performing it. I agree that generally such a term is by law imported into every contract." ... The implied undertaking not to do anything to hinder the other party from performing his part of the contract may, of course, be qualified by a term

express or to be implied from the contract and the surrounding circumstances. But the general duty remains save so far as qualified. It is difficult to conceive of a case in which this duty could be wholly excluded. ...

... it is well settled that the courts will imply a duty to do whatever is necessary in order to enable a contract to be carried out.'

5
Collaborative working arrangements

Any venture that involves working on a collaborative basis in a business context is potentially contentious. First, when forming the relationship, do the parties owe each other a duty of good faith? This point is addressed in section 5.1 below.

Second, when working collaboratively, what is the nature of the working relationship? The very expressions 'collaborative working', 'partnering' and 'joint ventures' do not refer specifically to contracts. One of the key questions can be whether there was an intention to create legal relations at all. An extension to that is the question whether, or to what extent, a partnering 'charter' is binding on the parties. Even if there were no failings and one party chooses to withdraw, an issue potentially arises as to whether compensation for the other party is due. This is discussed in section 5.2 below.

These are matters of concern, not least because they have arisen before the courts in disputes spanning several industries: new arrangements and structures bring new developments in law also. Those issues extend to differing payment arrangements which are considered in section 5.3 below. The arrangements range from cost or profit share to the opposite approach whereby the contractor undertakes to carry out all work for a 'Guaranteed Maximum Price'. As with all new arrangements, there has been little judicial consideration of these provisions, but to understand these points is of some importance when considering 'collaborating' under new arrangements.

5.1 GOOD FAITH IN NEGOTIATIONS

It is long established that a duty of good faith should not be implied in contracts under English Law: *Walford v Miles* (see section 1.3 above). The non-disclosure of material facts in negotiations, however morally questionable, does not create a cause of action. The leading proposition on the failure to disclose a material fact in negotiations was explained by Lord Atkin in *Bell v Lever Bros*. The case of *Conlon v Simms* shows how that was applied between partners in a partnership.

The case of *George Wimpey UK Ltd v VIC Construction Ltd* raises the interesting point as to whether a duty of good faith extends to a party who notices an error in the other party's pricing but continues to negotiate without mentioning the error. The court in *Thiess Contractors Pty Ltd v Placer (Granny Smith) Pty Ltd*, an Australian decision, found that good faith can extend to fairness in pricing.

By way of exception, good faith duties can apply to partners, and prospective partners, to partnerships. The point is of some relevance to parties considering joint venture arrangements. Equally, it is of note that the courts have alluded to the 'good faith' on the part of employers inviting tenders: See *Blackpool and Fylde Aero Club v Blackpool BC* (see also section 2.2 above) where the Court of Appeal made it clear that a party inviting tenders had a duty 'to act in good faith – not to issue a sham invitation', and *Harmon CFEM v House of Commons* (see section 2.2 above).

See also *Scott v Belfast Education & Library Board* at section 2.2 above.

Bell v Lever Brothers Ltd (1932)

Lord Atkin said:

'Ordinarily the failure to disclose a material fact which might influence the mind of a prudent contractor does not give the right to avoid the contract. The principle of caveat emptor applies outside contracts of sale. There are certain contracts expressed by law to be contracts of the utmost good faith, where material facts must be disclosed; if not, the contract is voidable. Apart from the special fiduciary relationships, contracts for partnership and contracts of insurance are the leading instances. In such cases the duty does not arise out of contract; the duty of a person proposing an insurance arises before a contract is made, so of an intending purchaser.'

Conlon v Simms (2006)

This case concerned a dispute between partners to a law firm. Lawrence Collins J held that a duty of good faith existed in a partnership context at the negotiations stage, even before the partnership was formed.

In the Court of Appeal, this point was upheld. Lord Justice Jonathan Parker added that there could be no doubt that the principle of caveat emptor did not apply to the making of a partnership agreement, and that in negotiating such an agreement a party owed a duty to the other negotiating parties to disclose all material facts of which he had knowledge and of which the other negotiating parties might not be aware. It therefore followed that prospective partners had a duty to disclose such material matters. In support, Lord Justice Jonathan Parker referred with approval to *Bell v Lever Brothers Ltd*.

George Wimpey UK Ltd v VIC Construction Ltd (2005)

VIC agreed to sell land to Wimpey. Wimpey made an error in its pricing. This became apparent to VIC, but not to Wimpey, during negotiations. Wimpey sought rectification for unilateral mistake. It was noted that the classic pathway to rectification was where the executed instrument is shown not to give effect to a prior accord or agreement as to its content. The mistake may be unilateral or bilateral.

Was this then a unilateral mistake on Wimpey's part? If a party's conduct amounts to deception or fraud, there is no need to resort to doctrines of mistake. Sedley LJ continued:

> 'There is, as it seems to me, a paradox in the notion of what an honourable and reasonable person would do in the context of an arm's-length commercial negotiation. This is a context in which honour (or honesty) and rationality (or reasonableness) are frequently not on speaking terms …

Take the present case. An honourable person negotiating for VIC would probably have asked Wimpey if they realised that E had been left out, but I very much doubt whether a reasonable negotiator would have done so. His first duty would have been to his own principal, whose interests undoubtedly lay in leaving E out and not alerting Wimpey to the omission.

The phrase "honest and reasonable" is not a term of art. It is a judicial attempt to sketch a line beyond which conduct may be regarded as unconscionable or inequitable. Its duality, however, is a recognition that honesty alone is too pure a standard for business dealings because it omits legitimate self-interest; while reasonableness alone is capable of legitimising Machiavellian tactics.

Mistake is a concept which sits awkwardly in this space. Absent a prior accord which has simply not been carried into effect, absent also a dishonest inducement to contract, one is looking for a mistake on the claimant's own part which the defendant was honour-bound, despite his own legitimate business interests, to point out to him. I am unable to accept that this was such a case on any tenable view of the evidence.

There are at least two kinds of mistake. One is a literal misunderstanding of some fact material to the proposed contract. The other is an error of judgment in entering into the contract. I find it difficult to think that the second kind has any relevance to the law of unilateral mistake. Nobody is bound, even in honour, to help his opposite number to negotiate to the best advantage.

What then was the material fact that Wimpey misunderstood? That E was omitted? They had only to look at VIC's draft to see that it was. Their mistake was failing to renegotiate it, and that seems to me an error of judgment, not of fact.

… I do not see how either honesty tempered with reasonableness or reasonableness tempered with honesty can have required VIC to point out to Wimpey where the latter's own best interests lay.

In saying this I recognise that sharp practice has no defined boundary. An arm's-length negotiation between parties of unequal competence and resources may well place greater constraints of honest and reasonable conduct on the stronger party than on the weaker. But the present case practically reverses the paradigm: it is the weaker party which is accused by the stronger of having unconscionably misled it by failing to draw the stronger party's attention to its own oversight.'

The general rule, as Slade LJ went on to say, is that in the absence of a duty to speak, mere silence or inaction is not such conduct as amounts to representation which will give rise to an estoppel. The difficulty lies in determining when such a duty arises.

'If ever a party was entitled to assume that its opponent knew what it was doing, it was VIC in its negotiations with one of the country's largest construction and development enterprises. In my judgment the mistake made by Wimpey was a result of their own corporate neglect for which VIC bore no legal or – so far as it matters – moral responsibility.'

Thiess Contractors Pty Ltd and Placer (Granny Smith) Pty Ltd (1999)

Placer (Granny Smith) Pty Ltd entered into a contract with Thiess Contractors Pty Ltd whereby Thiess would carry out mining operations for Placer at rates based on genuine estimates of the cost of its operation, plus an agreed profit margin of 5 per cent. Placer terminated the contract on the basis that the cost of continuing with Thiess under the existing contract was substantially higher than prices otherwise available on the market. Clause 1.1.5 of the contract required that Thiess and Placer act in good faith.

Thiess commenced action against Placer alleging wrongful termination and alternatively, Placer acted in bad faith in terminating the contract. Placer counterclaimed, alleging that it had overpaid Thiess because, in breach of the contract and despite its obligation of good faith, Thiess had deliberately inflated its estimates of costs to be incurred in carrying out the contract work.

The court found that good faith involves goodwill, cooperation and honesty between the parties and this extends to reasonableness and fairness in pricing. Per Templeman J:

'I construe the obligation of good faith as requiring the parties to act honestly with each other and to take reasonable steps to co-operate in relation to matters where the contract does not define rights and obligations or provide any mechanisms for the resolution of disputes. ... In relation to the interpretation of the Contract, the obligation of good faith is more difficult to define. I think it requires the parties to construe or give effect to general provisions in such a way as to promote the contractual objectives which are to be gleaned either from the contract as a whole or from the provision in particular.'

Harmon CFEM Facades (UK) Ltd v The Corporate Officer of the House of Commons (1999)

The case arose from construction of Portcullis House, a building to provide office accommodation for Members of Parliament. The employer wished as much work as possible to be carried out by UK firms. The cladding works were awarded to a British contractor. The claimant, a Canadian cladding business, claimed damages for breach of the implied contract said to arise from the requests for submission of tenders and the provision of a tender in response. HH Judge Humphrey LLoyd QC held that requests for the submission of tenders and the response created an implied contract, including an implied obligation to treat tenderers who responded equally and fairly.

(See also section 2.2 on contents of tender contract.)

5.2 PARTNERING RELATIONSHIPS

The execution of construction work under a partnering agreement is a comparatively recent phenomenon. Agreements of this nature appear in several forms. At one end of the range is a non-binding partnering charter that encourages collaborative behaviour on the part of project participants, such as that considered in *Birse v St David*. At the other end of the range are multi-project framework agreements which may simply be a vehicle through which standard terms are developed for work on several projects.

Two cases below (*Khan v Miah* and *Beddow v Cayzer*) provide some general guidance as to when a partnership might come into existence.

A further variant is the introduction within standard forms of a provision encouraging collaborative working. There are two provisions in standard forms. In PPC 2000, clause 1.1.3 says that the parties shall 'work together and individually in the spirit of trust, fairness and mutual cooperation for the benefit of the project'. In the NEC Engineering and Construction Contract (edition 3), clause 10.1 reads, 'The Employer, the Contractor, the Project Manager and the Supervisor shall act as stated in this contract and in a spirit of mutual trust and co-operation'.

A similar provision appeared in the contract in *Costain & Others v Bechtel*, where some comments were made with respect to whether impartiality in assessing valuations can be equated with good faith.

The cases in this section illustrate some of the difficulties in establishing whether a partnering relationship has been agreed *Profit Boat Development v Craft Projects* is a construction case from Hong Kong involving a main contractor and subcontractor. The other two cases, which arise from other industries, note that partnering relationships have been the subject of disputes elsewhere. Indeed, in *Baird v Marks & Spencer* the relationship between M&S and its supplier appears to have been a close working and product development relationship of the type now seen in the construction industry. The judgment in *McPhail & Anor v Bourne* was concerned with the nature of the relationship between four members of a 'boy band'. Whilst unrelated to construction, the judgment contains a discussion covering partnership law and returns to the question considered in *Birse* as to whether there was an intention, through the parties' relationship, to create legal relations.

Birse Construction Limited v St David Limited (1999)

St David was the developer of the Adventurers Quay development in Cardiff Bay. On 5 May 1997, contractors Birse Construction and clients St David Ltd attended a Team Building Seminar. They drew up and signed a Partnering Charter, with the overall stated aim: 'To produce exceptional quality development within the agreed time frame, at least cost, enhancing our reputations through mutual co-operation and trust'. The Partnering Charter contained a statement of detailed intentions.

On 14 November 1997, the parties expressed a 'common aim to sign the contract prior to the Christmas break'. On 5 March 1998, the client notified the contractor of its intention to deduct liquidated damages for delay. On 1 July 1998, practical completion of Phase 1A was certified. On 11 August 1998, the contractor left the site. The client treated this as abandonment; the contractor said there was no contract to abandon.

The issue was whether an enforceable agreement of any kind existed. On the evidence, the court was satisfied that the parties had never reached a concluded contract, and hence there was no provision that required the dispute between them to go to arbitration.

Khan v Miah (2000)

This was a case of an express agreement on a joint business venture. The parties had begun to implement the agreement but the business had not commenced trading. The House of Lords held that there was no rule of law that parties to a joint venture did not become partners until actual trading commenced.

Beddow v Cayzer (2006)

Tugendhat J held that a partnership at will came into existence on the basis of an opportunity to acquire shares, although there was no written agreement and the parties did not regard their relationship as a partnership.

Baird Textile Holdings Ltd v Marks & Spencer plc (2001)

Baird was a clothing supplier to M&S. It was had traded with M&S for 30 years and was a 'partnership supplier'. The working relationship of their businesses was very close. Without notice, M&S declared it would no longer engage Baird. Baird did not have a long-term agreement of any sort. Baird claimed that it could not terminate the supply arrangement without giving reasonable notice which, Baird argued, was three years.

The Court of Appeal held that a 30-year supply arrangement was not grounds for implying a contract between the parties where M&S had deliberately avoided entering a supply contract in order to preserve maximum flexibility in its trading arrangements.

Sir Andrew Morritt V-C concurred (as did Judge LJ and Mance LJ), finding that a contract could not be implied. Contracts are only implied where it is necessary. Here, any such agreement to keep up the purchase of clothes, subject to reasonable notice for termination, would be too uncertain. Uncertainty was confirmed by an absence of intention to be legally bound. Furthermore, an argument of estoppel could not succeed because estoppel is not capable (in English law as yet) of creating its own cause of action. Also, concerning estoppel, Judge LJ held that 'The interesting question ... is whether equity can provide a remedy which cannot be provided by contract. It seems clear that the principles of the law of estoppel have not yet been fully developed', questioning estoppel and the applicability of equity.

Profit Boat Development v Craft Projects (2007)

This Hong Kong case decided by the Court of First Instance was concerned with allegations made by one party as to the existence of an oral or implied joint venture agreement.

The court noted that generally speaking, the parties in an integrated joint venture combine their resources and share the profits and losses in an agreed proportion. On the other hand, in a non-integrated joint venture, each party takes on a specified scope of work and is responsible for the profits or losses associated with that particular scope of work.

AMEC-Hong Kong Construction was the main contractor in respect of the KCRC West Rail Yuen Long and Long Ping Station Contract No. 202 ('Contract No. 202'). By a letter dated 3 May 2000, Craft asked to be included in AMEC-HKC JV's database for subcontract works. By a letter dated 17 May 2000, AMEC-HKC JV invited the defendant to submit a lump sum fixed price for the supply and erection of the structural steel roof, aluminium cladding, skylight and ancillary fixtures for the Long Ping Station under Contract No. 202 ('subcontract work').

At the centre of this dispute is the plaintiff's contention that there was a joint venture agreement (JVA) between the plaintiff and the defendant in respect of the subcontract work. As is commonly known in the construction industry, a joint venture between two or more contractors may take many different forms, including the forms of integrated joint venture and non-integrated joint venture.

The subcontract work comprised two main elements: the structural steelwork ('steelwork') and the roof cladding work ('cladding work'). It is the plaintiff's case that a JVA was reached by the parties to form a non-integrated joint venture whereby: (1) the plaintiff and the defendant agreed to jointly and exclusively tender for and perform the subcontract work; (2) the plaintiff would be responsible for the steelwork while the defendant would be responsible for the cladding work.

No written joint venture agreement had ever been signed by the parties. The plaintiff's primary case was that an express oral JVA ('oral JVA') was reached between Mr Lee on behalf of the plaintiff and Mr Craft on behalf of the defendant at a meeting held on 26 May 2000. Alternatively, the plaintiff contended that the JVA was partly oral, partly in writing and partly by conduct in that the parties' dealings and conduct during the period from around 26 May 2000 to 11 July 2000 gave rise to a JVA ('implied JVA').

On the facts, the court found that the parties' conduct after 26 May 2000 and the contemporaneous documents were wholly inconsistent with the existence of the oral JVA contended for by the plaintiff.

As regards the implied JVA, the court said that the applicable test is the one set out in *Baird Textiles v Marks & Spencer*, where the learned judge considered other relevant authorities, including *Blackpool and Fylde Aero Club v Blackpool BC* (which dealt with the implication of a contract from a request for tenders and submission in response).

The court concluded that evidence and considerations discussed above in respect of the parties' contentions on the oral JVA are of equal relevance to the debate over the implied JVA. In particular, if the parties' conduct is inconsistent with the existence of an oral JVA, it was difficult to see how an implied JVA could have arisen.

> 'Having reviewed the evidence discussed above, I do not think it can be said that the parties' conduct is more consistent with the existence of a JVA than with its absence. Instead, the parties' conduct is more consistent

with the defendant's contention that at all material times it only treated the plaintiff as a potential subcontractor for the steelwork. Moreover, the implication of the alleged JVA is not necessary to give business reality to the commercial relationship between the plaintiff and the defendant. In the circumstances, I find that there was no implied JVA.'

McPhail & Anor v Bourne & Anor (2008)

The claimants and defendants were singers who had formed a band. One of the issues was whether their collaboration was legally binding as a contract or a partnership at will.

The claimants put their case for the existence of an agreement on the basis of an express oral agreement, alternatively, an agreement to be implied from their conduct.

In the judgment, it was noted that section 1 of the *Partnership Act* 1890 defines a 'partnership' as 'the relation which exists between persons carrying on a business in common with a view to profit'. That definition did not refer to the existence of any contract between the partners. However, as the House of Lords had noted, a partnership is a consensual arrangement based on agreement and it is clear from the context that Lord Millett was referring to an agreement which had contractual force and effect. Thus, it is a precondition to the existence of a partnership that there is a binding contractual relationship between the parties and the law will then determine whether that contract is a contract of partnership or creates some other relationship.

> 'The agreement which is necessary for the existence of a partnership need not be an express agreement. The existence of such an agreement may be implied from the conduct of the parties. If, for example, two or more persons carried on a business in common with a view to profit and distributed the net income of that business between them, it may well be appropriate to imply the existence of a contract between them, the terms of which contract provided for those persons to carry on that business and to have rights and obligations in relation to that business and the benefits and the liabilities to which it gave rise.'

Mr Justice Morgan said:

'... in my judgment, in a case where the choice for the court is between holding that there was no intention to create contractual relations at all and holding that there was an intention to create a contract terminable at will, it is difficult to see why the parties would see it as necessary to have an informal contract terminable at will as compared with no contractual relationship at all, with the matter resting on a social relationship and a great deal of optimism, which no doubt existed. Furthermore, in relation to the suggested express agreement, and an obligation of good faith imposed on the parties, there would have been a lack of clarity as to what would and what would not be permitted in those respects.'

In this case, it was held that the lack of definition in relation to the activities which were the subject of the contract and the alleged partnership and, indeed, the complete lack of appreciation that anything the parties were doing required them to address those questions, suggested that there was no intention to create a contractual relationship at all.

Costain Ltd & Ors v Bechtel Ltd & Anor (2005)

The claimant contractor entered into a contract to provide civil engineering and construction works for the extension and refurbishment of St Pancras Station in London, part of the Channel Tunnel High-Speed Rail Link Project. Recital L to the contract provided as follows:

'The Employer, the Contractor and the Project Manager act in the spirit of mutual trust and co-operation and so as not to prevent compliance by any of them with the obligations each is to perform under the Contract.'

Issues arose as to whether the defendant project manager had a duty to act impartially when assessing sums payable: There were allegations that the project manager had acted in this regard in bad faith. Jackson J concentrated on the question whether there was a duty of impartiality and whether, arguably, that duty was breached.

In a preliminary hearing as to whether an injunction should be issued, Mr Justice Jackson did not address Recital L directly, but added some comments with respect to the phrase 'in good faith', by adding:

'... this phrase is ambiguous. Sometimes it is used as a synonym for "impartially". Sometimes it is used as a synonym for "honestly". ... A semantic debate about the precise meaning of the phrase "in good faith" in the context of certification seems to me to serve no useful purpose.'

5.3 PAYMENT IN COLLABORATIVE WORKING ARRANGEMENTS AND GUARANTEED MAXIMUM PRICE

5.3.1 Target costs, painshare/gainshare

Under a target cost contract, the parties agree a target cost and agree between them to share, in a predetermined proportion, the difference between the target cost and the actual outturn cost or final account amount. Hence, if the final account exceeds the target cost, both parties share the overrun (the 'painshare') or if the final account shows a saving overall, both parties might share the saving (the 'gainshare').

Several standard forms are available to support this arrangement. In *Alstom Signaling Ltd (t/a Alstom Transport Information Solutions) and Jarvis Facilities Ltd*, the parties had failed to agree the percentages at which the cost overrun or saving was to be shared. The case showed the extent to which the court was prepared to determine those sharing arrangements on the parties' behalf.

Alstom Signaling Ltd (t/a Alstom Transport Information Solutions) and Jarvis Facilities Ltd (2004)

This was a dispute between Alstom and Jarvis in relation to the interpretation of a subcontract between them to extend the Tyne & Wear Metro. The main issue that arose was whether a contract contained a pain/gain sharing arrangement and, if so, whether the court could determine its terms where details of that arrangement were unclear and had not been finalised.

The court decided that the parties could not agree whether the main contract pain/gainshare mechanism should be applicable but that the parties had intended to be bound by arrangements of this type, although they had not decided on the final mechanism for achieving this object. In such a case, the court should assist the parties to adjust the relevant matters and the working out of their contracts so as to preserve rather than destroy the bargain.

Mr. Recorder Reese QC held that there was an agreement in principle that the contract would contain a pain/gainshare provision but that the parties had not reached agreement of the precise detail of that arrangement. Accordingly, there was nothing to prevent the court resolving the difference between the parties as to what was a fair and reasonable mechanism by which the parties would share any pain/gain.

In summary, 'what can be made certain is itself certain'. The court took the view that the parties had reached agreement in all essential terms and that a pain/gain mechanism was an 'inessential' sub-contract term in the sense that the sub-contract could operate without it. However, the working out of the mechanism was deferred for further submissions.

A clear distinction was drawn between this type of case and that where the parties have simply not reached agreement at all on crucial issues, leaving payment on a quantum meruit basis and implied obligations as to quality.

5.3.2 Guaranteed Maximum Price

Since the late 1990s, there have been references within reports of parties having agreed to carry out work on a Guaranteed Maximum Price, or GMP, basis. It would appear that no universal definition has evolved.

Definitions in usage range from all-in agreements whereby the contractor undertakes to carry out work accepting all risks, to those where the GMP is a contract sum subject to adjustment for all client changes or acts of prevention. Mr Justice Lindsay attempted to define the GMP arrangement in *Jarvis Interiors Ltd v Galliard Homes Ltd.* An interesting example appeared in *Skanska Construction UK Ltd v Egger (Barony) Ltd* of the type of contract provisions used. As the *City Inn v Shepherd Construction* case shows, there may be complex, and disputed, interaction between the GMP and other provisions, in that case the value engineering proposals made in tenders.

A recurring feature of disputes arising from use of a letter of intent is reference to the parties agreeing a GMP. In *George Fisher Holdings Ltd*, for example, the letter of intent stated an intention to negotiate a GMP. An agreement to negotiate is not enforceable. An additional difficulty in provisions of this type is that the detailed payment mechanism under which the GMP operates is not provided, making the entire provision void for uncertainty. Contrary to the term 'guaranteed', these provisions are typically a contract sum provision to which changes are permitted in limited circumstances. The provision in *Emcor Drake & Scull Ltd v Edinburgh Royal Joint Venture & others*, for example, was noted variously as being a GMP or target price and was to be subject to variations as the work proceeded.

Jarvis Interiors Ltd v Galliard Homes Ltd (2000)

Jarvis contracted to build 36 flats for Galliard in London's Docklands area. The contract was to be based on the *JCT Standard Form (1980 edition)* (private without quantities) incorporating standard and bespoke amendments. A new Article 7 was to read:

> 'Guaranteed Maximum Price – for the avoidance of doubt this contract is deemed to be let on a Guaranteed Maximum Price basis, and therefore, all references to variations and fluctuations contained therein are deemed to be deleted.'

Commenting on this in the Court of Appeal, Mr Justice Lindsay noted:

> 'The term "Guaranteed Maximum Price" there twice mentioned was not defined in the Preliminaries or in the Articles, nor is it one of the over 50 terms defined in the JCT 80 conditions. Nor is it, as transpired in argument, even a term of art in the construction industry in this country.'

Evans LJ found that there was no agreement. One of the reasons given was as follows:

> '… it is not possible to be certain what the terms of the contract were. The meaning and effect of "guaranteed maximum price" are tied up with the parties' intention as

to the scope of the work to be carried out and in particular, in a context such as this, as to the extent to which, if any at all, the variations would be permitted, consistently with the "guaranteed maximum" price which was agreed. What their intentions were was left uncertain ... and this uncertainty, in my judgment, was such as to prevent an enforceable contract coming into being. I could also agree with the judge's conclusion that "there was no meeting of the minds between the parties" if, as I understand, he meant that, notwithstanding the handshake and the parties' beliefs, they were insufficiently agreed.'

Skanska Construction UK Ltd v Egger (Barony) Ltd (2002)

The parties agreed a GMP contract. A GMP was agreed but was subject to adjustment. There was provision for valuation of variations, with the value of omissions being by reference to amounts in the GMP analysis. Also, loss and expense was payable if compliance with employer's instructions

'... unavoidably results in the regular process of the Works or any Section or part thereof being materially disrupted or prolonged and in consequence of such disruption or prolongation the Contractor properly and directly incurs any expense in performing the Contract which he would not otherwise have incurred and which is beyond that otherwise provided for in or reasonably contemplated by the Contract, the Guaranteed Maximum Price shall, subject to Clause 26(2), be increased by the amount of that expense.'

City Inn Ltd v Shepherd Construction Ltd (2007)

City Inn engaged Shepherd Construction to build a new hotel in Bristol. The agreement contained reference to a GMP. In this case, that was more akin to a contract sum, as clause 14.5 provided for adjustment of the GMP in respect of three matters: provisional sums; contingencies and day work; and unforeseen or unknown ground conditions. There was a dispute as to whether the estimated cost of 'value engineering' savings fell within the GMP.

Lord Drummond Young noted that the contractor had, no doubt, arrived at the lowest tender price by taking the value engineering savings into account. He said:

'... a "business gamble" is involved, but that is true of any tender. The Guaranteed Maximum Price premium seems to me to be just that: the contractor agreed to a cap on the price for the Works, subject to certain defined exceptions, but took a premium in exchange. The VE savings were taken into account in determining the Guaranteed Maximum Price, but that merely emphasizes the point made above: the savings were reflected in the calculation of the total Contract Sum, with all the consequences that that entails. That seems to me to point to the proposition that the VE Proposals were included in the contract Works. As to the suggestion that the VE proposals were designed to maximize the contractor's profit, it appears to me that they were designed essentially to reduce the tender price; whether this resulted in a greater profit would depend upon a range of factors as the contract proceeded. If the VE Proposals formed part of the parties' contract, any rejection of a proposal would amount to a variation, with a potential impact on the total amount payable by the employer, and also a potential impact on the contractor's profit. That it cannot be said that that was any "onus" on the contractor to have VE Proposals accepted; they might or might not increase its profit, although they would certainly make its tender price more competitive.'

Index

The *Case in Point* series

The *Case in Point* series is a popular set of concise practical guides to legal issues in land, property and construction. Written for the property professional, they get straight to the key issues in a refreshingly jargon-free style.

Areas covered:

Party Walls
Item code: 7269
Published: May 2004

Estate Agency
Item code: 7472
Published: July 2004

Rent Review
Item code: 8531
Published: May 2005

Expert Witness
Item code: 8842
Published: August 2005

Lease Renewal
Item code: 8711
Published: August 2005

VAT in Property and Construction
Item code: 8840
Published: September 2005

Construction Adjudication
Item code: 9040
Published: October 2005

Dilapidations
Item code: 9113
Published: January 2006

Planning Control
Item code: 9391
Published: April 2006

Building Defects
Item code: 9949
Published: July 2006

Contract Administration
Item code: 16419
Published: March 2007

Construction Claims
Item code: 16978
Published: December 2007

Easements and Other Rights
Item code: 17245
Published: March 2008

Negligence in Valuations and Surveys (2nd edition)
Item code: 17550
Published: August 2008

Service Charges (2nd edition)
Item code: 17456
Published: August 2008

Rights to Light
Item code: 7270
Published: October 2008

If you would like to be kept informed when new *Case in Point* titles are published, please e-mail **rbmarketing@rics.org**

All RICS Books titles can be ordered direct by:

☎ Telephoning 0870 333 1600

🖑 Online at www.ricsbooks.com

🖶 E-mail mailorder@rics.org